TWO'S COMPANY

Best wishes,
Monica.

HParcel.

'...she had thought to do without love, only to be shown that love was on offer to those who knew how to deal with it.'
(*Anita Brookner:* Undue Influence)

TWO'S COMPANY

Love Again: a Woman's Journey

HÉLÈNE PASCAL

Tivoli Books

Copyright © Hélène Pascal 2011
First published in 2011 by Tivoli Books
53a Primrose Gardens, London NW3 4UL

Distributed by Gardners Books, 1 Whittle Drive, Eastbourne, East
Sussex, BN23 6QH
Tel: +44(0)1323 521555 | Fax: +44(0)1323 521666

www.helenepascal.co.uk

British Library Cataloguing in Publication Data
A catalogue record for this book is available from the British
Library.

ISBN 978-0-9567621-0-8

Typeset by Amolibros, Milverton, Somerset
www.amolibros.com
This book production has been managed by Amolibros
Printed and bound by T J International Ltd, Padstow, Cornwall, UK

Acknowledgements

It is my heart's duty to thank the many people who have, in their diverse ways, supported and helped me make this book happen:

First of all, my friend Judith Robinson who did the editing work and is therefore the godmother of this baby; Gabi Braun and Trudy Graves who rescued me during my disagreements with the computer, abandoning man and child; Mick and Colette Hogan who were the first to read the book, and whose encouragement gave me faith; and also Alan Ferrett, Ruth Levene, Fran Markotic, Angela Bell, Hina Pandya and Ruth Posner, all my lovely friends.

I have a debt to the London publishers who gave me such a crooked contract that I decided to go it alone, and Jane Tatam at Amolibros who rescued me, giving me the benefit of her experience and wisdom.

For Isabelle and Bradley, who have found each other.

Chapter One

I am sixty-six years old: do not imagine too many wrinkles on my face, I have few, and people laugh when I declare my age. I look no older than in my fifties and still enjoy the privilege of being attractive. While small – I am five foot two – I do not feel at all small or fragile. Gravity, inexorably, does its deed, although my size is average and my shape overall quite good.

No longer being twenty, or even thirty, is certainly an advantage: I was resilient but ill-equipped in those days, gifted more with coping mechanisms than clarity. What wisdom I may have acquired is now regretfully accompanied with sadness and some cynicism, but because my blood courses healthily in my veins, I respond to sunshine and can still run and dance easily. When I attend the gym and exercise exhilarates my body, something joyful comes into play. Which makes the "life situation" all the more sore: I live alone, which can be a blessing (no one to bother me) although often too much of a good thing, particularly at weekends when my friends are busy with their own families. Holiday times are a painful curse, everyone seems to go on holiday in couples or with their children and grandchildren except for me: apart from one grown-up daughter here in London and two vague cousins in France, I have no family. My daughter is the light of my life and a success story, but she lives with her boyfriend and has her own life, as it should be.

'Join groups!' say my friends, and advise day and evening classes, reading groups, language clubs, poetry workshops... . All very well, but however many – single – friends, usually of the same sex, I might make after some months, I would still find myself on my own most weekends (others will have families, an old parent...) and the Christmas and summer holiday periods make an exile of me, the time when I feel abandoned, unseen, unloved, unjustly unappreciated, and I rage and curse and grieve.

So what choice do I have? I say this grudgingly. I resent having to do this exercise as it may just be an excursion; I may shirk engagement and shrink and withdraw, having found the water too cold or hot, the current too strong; can't be bothered; too much hassle. It may of course also be fun: I catch myself chuckling: not dead yet, just give me a little amusement, a diversion, a recreation: for Heaven's sake, a little joy! Here my wisdom whispers: do not play with other people's feelings. And although they may be playing with mine, we are all tentative on this stage, we juggle with clouds...

Call me pragmatic by all means: it has to be done, and I would think about it less, calculate less, if this enterprise was simply born out of neediness, but I am no longer the romantic absolutist I used to be (too old, too worn out); so I have to be practical, efficient, and most of all realistic: common sense should have a crucial role to play, although I have a nagging suspicion that the senses, sensibility, and sensuality might eventually find their voice.

The approach is matter-of-fact, focusing in a hard-headed way on the main point of this endeavour: select, not merely find, a worthy lover of my feistiness, a friend indulgent of my presumptions, a willing but not subservient escort in my ventures, a knowledgeable field guide to the new terrain, aware of the inevitable pitfalls, a kind teacher of his own experiences.

*

I have selected two advertisements so far. The first one says:

> – WELL-TRAVELLED, intelligent arts lover, retired, fit, solvent, sensual, seeks best friend and lover, probably 50s, n /s. London.

I judge it well-balanced, mature, honest. So far. I myself love the arts – indeed I have collected quality paintings and sculptures all my life and frequently go to exhibitions. 'Retired' means he will have leisure. The rest: 'fit, solvent, sensual' is reassuring if it is true. I know people lie: didn't I myself claim six years ago to be many years younger? And I lie a lot less than most, I am in fact quite scrupulous in this domain. So I shall ring him, or rather the voice box number given by the newspaper, in order to hear his longer spoken message, to which I will then decide to reply or not.

The second one is even better:

> – DINNER COMPANION WANTED by Cambridge graduate, 58, enjoys human nature, conversation and irony. If you are interesting, attractive and hungry, please call.

I am seduced by the humour, the evident maturity and the word 'conversation': give me good conversation any time, I am hungry for it. As for hungry, God knows I can eat, and there are few things better than good food in good company. I want a date now, and cannot wait to hear his spoken message, but number one comes first.

*

'My name is Peter,' he says on his recorded message. He is sixty-two and lives in south-west London. He has worked in many countries and is a practical man as well as a lover of the arts. He is socially and politically aware and writes articles. His message is longer but this is all I am able to jot down and remember. His voice is educated without being 'posh' – a self-made man possibly? – I instantly envy his travels although they were for his work: maybe he no longer wishes to travel? I worry; though possibly he still loves it, wants to see more of the world, can I come too? We can talk politics.

I decide to leave a reply, describing myself as a professional woman, humorous, an arts lover too; I love books and nature alike and relish a good conversation on politics, social issues as well as psychology; I adore gardens and have a beautiful one myself; I am looking for a relationship based on friendship and mutual interests.

'My name is Ross,' says number two. He is asking for a dinner partner because he is a good listener, interested in people. He likes books, particularly by female authors like Anita Brookner and Barbara Pym: he likes the way women write about emotions, they get much closer to the truth, much more subtly, than male writers. He used to have a practice (he must be a doctor), but now lives and works in central London as an adviser to the government. He loves the buzz of London and keeps fit. He is a Taurean.

I like the way he talks, fluent and witty, and it so happens

I love Anita Brookner and have at least five of her books on my shelves. I leave a message, but press the wrong key and it is erased. I repeat it – at £1.20 a minute this is getting pricey. In my haste I am afraid I sound a little muddled. Did I give my telephone number? I say, twice, 'In any case, I wish you luck.' Silly woman. I hope he calls.

When I tell my daughter of my enterprise, she is outraged, understandable because she is both young and old-fashioned: she wishes me to keep busy, get a job of sorts, instead of looking for a man to sort my life out. She misses the point, I feel, but being a loyal daughter she still cares and asks: "Did you say you were pretty?" As it happens, I have forgotten. Ah, well...

Peter is the first to ring, the very next day: he sounds friendly enough, at ease, and is a fluent talker. We have a lot of things in common, apart from squirrels – a whole crowd of them seem to live in my garden – whom I love and he hates. Living in Dulwich, he is at the opposite end of the map to me. He has travelled widely and had even met Osama Bin Laden ("He was young at the time."). I certainly want to hear more about that – and about the fact that he writes for a right-wing journal: I would've dropped him instantly in the past on account of this alone as I think that our political choices come from a disposition of the heart, but I have become more tolerant, it is a question of degree – and we could have a good debate! Since we decide to meet this coming Sunday at Embankment station and he will be holding *The Sunday Times*, I shall make a show of my *Observer*. We may even laugh about it.

The next time he calls, we decide on a time and talk little: he is tired, slept badly last night, he is going straight to bed. Did he worry, I wonder. These exercises can be nerve-racking if you are both needy and dependent on hope. For my part, hope isn't an emotion that I consider useful or even easy to come by nowadays, so I sleep like a log.

– Two-thirty inside the station, it's too cold to wait outside, we shall go and have a coffee somewhere nearby. What do you look like?

– I'm five foot two and blonde with short hair, and I'll be wearing a beige coat. And, by the way, my daughter tells me to say I'm pretty! I laugh.

– Really? You have told your daughter?

– Yes, and she completely disapproves of me!

– Oh, dear! Well, you could tell her she can come as a chaperone! Now, I am five foot ten, with white hair and a beard, and I shall be wearing a black coat.

That sounds rather smart.

*

I arrive on time and he is already there. At first glance I know I will not like him: there is something severe about him, apart from the fact that he is very unattractive: a swollen red lower lip hangs low on his face, giving him a disdainful look. Well, he didn't describe himself as good-looking so there is no betrayal there. I brace myself for an hour of dutiful conversation, but I mustn't be dismissive, he is an intelligent man.

– You are Hélène?

– Yes, hello Peter.

There is a twinkle in his eyes and he kisses me dryly on both cheeks. Why kiss me when we have never met before? I have no wish to be kissed. Does he think it's the done thing? What's wrong with shaking hands?

Almost as soon as we come out of the station, he ushers me into the first café we encounter, a crowded and noisy place full of chattering women, the worst possible place for a leisurely first conversation, but I notice an empty table away from the crowd near the window and call him over. As it hasn't yet been cleared, he makes a big show, in a disgruntled way, of stacking up the dirty plates and the cutlery, the cups and saucers, finally sitting down. I put the *Observer* in my bag, he will have noticed it and I get a sense that he will have decided it set the tone: I was of 'the other side', a woolly liberal if not a dreadful leftie, he was wasting his time because he cannot stand these people. It's possibly the reason why he took me to this ghastly café. True, he had given me a clue when saying he wrote articles for a right-wing journal, but there are shades of right, and the subsequent *Sunday Times* didn't seem to announce anything very terrible. However, I feel a coldness in him, and I feel cold too, like a grown-up who knows certain things have to be done, patiently gone through with decorum and good manners if possible.

So we talk: he parked his car nearby; the advantages of London, so much to offer; the arts (he attends History of Art classes); gardens; squirrels and how to stop them eating the bird food. He doesn't laugh at all or even smile, and yet I have these lovely stories of blackbirds flying towards me for more raisins, and a squirrel sitting on the orangery chair... . They would be wasted on him, as was my initial mention of Dennis Healy, a very old man now, being interviewed with his wife on this morning's television current affairs programme. The mere mention of the old Labour adversary causes such a haughty expression of scorn that it stops me in my tracks. Dennis Healy had spoken of his love of photography and poetry and I was going to ask: did he like poetry too? I feel scolded. Obviously politics wasn't far away, was waiting to emerge, we are both political beings, interested in ideas and keen to take the measure of each other. But where humour would have allowed an entertaining and possibly friendly debate, his sneers and obvious contempt, matched by my stubbornness and defiance are an admission not only of defeat but of enmity.

He asked not a single question about me, my life or my daughter, even though I questioned him about his career, travels and tastes: our disagreements about young criminals, sentencing and education turned to open conflicts when we broached New Labour: what has Tony Blair done? Just tell me one thing! he almost barks. – Well, the minimum wage for a start! – What? Five pounds twenty-five? – A good deal more than it had been for ages! – In any case, most of his policies have been Conservative! – I know, that's why I don't particularly like him!

The red lip has fallen lower still, the corners of his mouth are down, the contempt palpable: he is cross, and I am almost enjoying making this arrogant man angry.

He has drunk his coffee, me my hot chocolate; I was offered no cakes. We had talked on the telephone of going to the National Gallery, and it seems it is still on, neither of us wanting to have completely wasted our time or be rude by deliberately shortening the encounter.

– What would you like to see? he asks.

– I'm easy, there is so much that's good. How about seeing the Vermeers and then some Post-Impressionists? I think he no longer cares, he is simply being courteous. We are both going through the motions and know it, it won't be difficult.

– I think I should go home now, he declares flatly when we have finished.

– I've a bus just around the corner, I reply.

– I'll be in touch, he adds in a manner of goodbye and kisses me again, if one can call it that, two dry and ill-humoured pecks on my cheeks.

– Oh, no, you won't, I nearly retort, but say, clearly:

– I wish you good luck, Peter, bye.

That was it. Quite painless really. And I've seen enough of The National Gallery today to know that I want to come back soon and alone, at leisure.

*

The Dinner Companion hasn't returned my call: did I press the required key at the end of my message? I fear not. Shall I ring him again? Maybe he is too busy now, dinner every night for a month at least, there are lots of very good women out there. I liked his voice and humour, his charm in fact. Beware of charm, I counsel myself, it can be a trap – but so can every good attribute: so is there no alternative to good luck? For this is what I need, seeing that, as my daughter reminds me: "You always pick the wrong one" – including her father, she would agree, since he is as poor a father to her as he was a partner to me, a spitting image of my own father…I had met him at a party, but it seems I no longer go to parties nor do I give them. The world had shrunk, and as I try to manipulate luck, I will very likely end up succumbing to fate yet again; after all, who were the fairies at the side of my crib? Mummy-daddy, mummy-daddy, blindfold, whispering their sad wishes…

Chapter Two

The first time I ventured on the territory of encounters from a newspaper page was a year or two after my daughter's birth, over twenty-four years ago. It had been desperately sad coming home after work to a small child alone, with no one to share my daily joy at her discovery, have adult conversations with, no one who cared. I also knew, though, that a relationship was best left aside, for a long while possibly, for there was work to be done: I had to shed the skin and heart of the needy child I was and re-shape myself into a strong and confident – self-loving – woman, no longer capable of falling victim to immature and sadistic men. A tall order. But I remember meeting one man in a hotel lounge, who recited at length French nineteenth-century verse at me, and at one point hammered the table with his fist, declaring with passion: 'I want to live for ever!!'

I refrained from suggesting he may be disappointed.

When, after ten years of hard work on myself and celibacy, I met a nice man on holiday, I was at least reassured that I had progressed to the point where I could be treated lovingly at last, and felt lucky that, 'at my age' – sixteen years ago then – I had found someone decent, dependable and a good friend. He could show my young daughter that fathers (he had two nice grown-up daughters of his own) and therefore men, could be kind, trustworthy and safe. The fact that Paul and I seemed to have the same tastes seemed serendipitous to begin with; but I soon realised that he only agreed with me on all matters because he amounted to very little, and desperately depended on merging with a woman and her approval to have any sense of himself. I came to understand that he had, in his childhood years during the war, acted as his mother's little husband during his father's long absence. This had been a time of bliss for him until his father's return, when his parents were happily reunited and he lost his role overnight, to be told to go and play outside.

I tried long and hard to convince myself that his qualities were all that mattered and, at 'my age', I should be thankful and sensible, but the shallowness of our conversations, the fact that we couldn't 'meet' as human beings and the platitudes that I was subjected to, were more than I could take.

Several years later I had finally put an end to my teaching career and since I had re-trained as a counsellor and no longer needed a large house, we moved to a smaller, cheaper one in a 'difficult' area. My daughter was finishing school, taking her 'A' levels and would soon be going to university; it crept up on me that I would no longer be an acting mother: a chapter was at its end, my lovely girl had grown her own wings, and I shouldn't be alone. A great void loomed ahead. It had been easy to fill my life with my daughter and my work and the house was often full of young people, but as with a cast in a play, everyone would leave after the curtain came down and a ruthless silence would occupy my space.

I had no friends who weren't married or gay, and didn't

myself frequent pubs or clubs of any kind except for a poetry workshop I had been invited to join by two of its members one evening: they had heard me read – a three minutes performance – at The Poetry Café. I was flattered and thrilled: so I was a real poet, and the workshops helped me progress. I got acquainted with an older poet who had taken a fancy to me, an Oxbridge man of some culture and hopefully self-knowledge (he had undergone several years of Jungian therapy after his divorce). Whilst he visited and brought chocolates and we shared a meal at his place or mine, I came to know some of his life story: he had been retired a few years from a job in industry and had recently separated from a woman he had lived with for some years after his divorce, a strange and irrational woman who kept accusing him of 'making things go wrong in the house'; he was well out of it. I sympathised with this pleasant, educated man, whilst knowing that all I wanted from him was decent conversation: he would be short-changed, since it was obvious he was after a great deal more. Talking to my friends, I have often jokingly described men of my age and older to be rather 'dusty' in the main: the way they so often age without keeping any shred of liveliness; their shuffling walk, the dull skin and eyes. Roger was rather dusty-looking to me, certainly unattractive and it never occurred to me that we would ever get close physically, the idea was rather repellent to me.

One evening, as we were sitting on my sofa talking of matters unrelated to any possibility of licentiousness, I was taken aback when he suddenly flipped, like a fish on the slab, and attempted to embrace me. I jumped back, primly crying out:

"No! No!" until he settled down again. We resumed the conversation for a while, a little dazed. I offered some more tea, politely pretending I wished to prolong the evening, but after visiting my bathroom yet again he announced he would make his way home.

If I was quite relieved after his departure, I was also amused by this incident, and got ready to go to bed: I undressed and washed my face, knowing I very probably wouldn't see Roger again socially. Ah, well, such was life. When I tried to flush the toilet, nothing happened: the handle was limp. Being of a practical nature, I lifted the lid of the cistern, to discover that the rubber piece that links the lever to the siphon had been removed and lay at the bottom. This is when I remembered his 'absurd and irrational' mistress, the one who accused him of making things go wrong in the house, with a certain sympathy...

This incident left me perplexed: how do we know others, the ones we love, the ones we choose to live with, when such a small episode as this suddenly throws open a whole, unseen aspect to the person, a streak of pettiness, malevolence even, irrational at that – a dark poltergeist? I had known this man for years, we had poetry friends in common: when do we actually know people? If there was a lesson here, it was possibly that we never truly knew them. Picking someone out of the pages of a newspaper could hardly be more hazardous: they would naturally be economical with the facts, and besides, however much we may wish to tell others the truth about ourselves, we may not always know that truth...

*

A few weeks later I decided to put a small ad in *The Sunday Times* rather than scour other people's every week: it seemed to be the more practical solution since, at the time, the replies were always in the form of letters rather than spoken messages as they are now. A letter told you so much: the envelope, the colour if any; the kind of paper; typewritten or not; then the hand-writing, the script, the layout; the style finally: how fluent, seemingly perceptive or sincere; the amount or lack of detail; where the emphasis lay: on the material, the spiritual, the intellectual? Like Miss Marple I would study, gauge, speculate, analyse, discard, and if I was lucky, select. But this was only the first round: one would have to meet some prospective candidates, with the proviso that the applicant was himself free to select or discard you after that meeting. It became a two-way exercise in which equality was restored.

I described myself as French-born, university educated, intelligent, attractive; a lover of art and gardens; attentive to others, a reader of books; I wished to meet a similarly-inclined man to be my friend and lover. I lied about my age, declaring fifty-one years instead of fifty-nine. (I suspect this is common after a certain age, most people thinking they look a great deal younger – I counted myself among them. On admitting the truth at the first or second encounter, the other person was meant to say: 'But you don't look it at all!')

I received nearly thirty replies, and I suspect the word 'French' to have been the reason for a larger number than expected, as I counted about a dozen letters telling me in clumsy French of their love of France and French cuisine – inevitably, they thought I was a good cook, if only they knew... . A few, in their apparent, excited comments, have been thinking of a French maid with a little white apron. Photographs are enclosed even though I haven't asked for any: one little old man in his kitchen, another one with his dog; a nice-looking man photographed many years ago, unless he still wears these clothes; a severe-looking prison warden type rants at length about our immoral times; a friendly and educated businessman; a film director; a French lawyer who lives in Birmingham; a witty teacher, lover of fast cars; a valuer of works of art; and the man who writes on a page torn from a notepad accompanied by a photo of himself naked to the top of his pubic hair, showing off his muscles.... What fun, I thought, all this could make a book!

My heart, however, wasn't in writing, my days were full and my attention elsewhere, and my heart sank at the prospect of actually ringing, then meeting some of these men. We were all lonely. The prospect of an encounter with a stranger brought that feeling acutely to the fore; seeking someone to fulfil your needs suddenly displayed it all into too bright a light; and our needs are our weaknesses, needy woman beware.... But we were all lonely, I repeated to myself, so why be fearful?

The teacher was very convivial but lightweight (we have but a short time to judge; we have to be ruthless, economical as well as candid, which doesn't exclude friendliness). Besides, there is, I discover with time, a brotherhood of lonely hearts, we may therefore be tactful, protective even: the art valuer was shy like a young man, this may be his first time; he made me feel like an understanding aunt and I ordered an apple crumble with two spoons, in order to break down a few barriers. He lived by himself in a house outside a provincial town, admitted to feeling isolated. As we talked of the lovely English countryside and the appeal of certain places, he became animated and disclosed a passion for York, the way he felt such affinities with it, as if he had lived there in a previous life. Sensing an opportunity, I went into problem-solving mode:

– Is there any reason why you live where you do? Any relatives? Friends?

– No...

– Is there any reason at all why you couldn't live elsewhere?

– Not really…

– Can you imagine yourself driving to York next Saturday, visiting a few estate agents and getting some details of properties in the areas you like?

He laughed, beguiled.

– Don't you think you could change your life? Isn't it entirely in your hands at present, since you have no ties? You could sell the present house where you feel lonely and live in that beautiful town you love…you'd explore it, make friends, join clubs, and meet a lovely lady…. What do you think? Is it possible?

– I guess so, yes, it is…. He looked at once thoughtful and stunned: new images of life were presenting themselves to him, he could see that novelty wasn't necessarily outlandish.

As we parted with great friendliness that afternoon, it didn't seem to me that the day had been wasted.

The businessman was quite remarkable, with the self-assurance both of education and a life well-lived. Through a career in industry he had managed to keep his conscience and idealism intact. After a successful divorce that left him friendly with his ex-wife and children, he felt he had still a lot to give. Honesty in relationships was a must, we agreed; in fact we agreed on so much I was really disheartened that I didn't feel at all attracted to him physically, indeed he could have been a well-loved brother. I guessed that asking for friendship now, when we were both on a quest for love was changing the rules in mid-course, it shouldn't be done, should it? But we were having dinner in a Greek restaurant, the evening was still a success, and he sent me postcards from his journeys for a while…

Chapter Three

My 'Dinner Companion' hasn't rung back and I am disappointed. I must have done something silly like pressed the wrong key and erased the whole message, that would be quite in character. I toy with the idea of ringing again, but what if my message had reached him and he thinks I'm desperate? I feel I could have great conversations with this man – Ross is his name – and wouldn't the world be a better place if we all had conversations with each other instead of the dreadful silence we live in? His voice itself was entrancing. It reached my soul...yes, I know how dangerous a voice can be.

I will ring him. I have nothing to lose. I am too old to care about risks. I carefully follow the procedure this time, listen to his message again, then speak in turn:

– Hello, Ross, it's Hélène again. I'm afraid I missed pressing some keys last time I rang, so I am just making sure I do it properly this time. And just in case we don't meet, since you mentioned Anita Brookner, I thought I'd tell you about Hilary Mantel who is the most extraordinary writer: start with *Giving up the Ghost* which is a memoir, very subtle and funny – and poignant about childhood. Also her short stories, *Learning to Talk*...

There are a hundred possible conversations about books alone, I know. While I speak to him, a few pips warn me of someone trying to get through, my daughter probably. At the end of my call, I dial 1471 to hear an unfamiliar number. I call it straight away and Ross's voice appears through the ether, oozing smoothness and charm: he apologises for being late in replying:

– You must be all dined out by now! I joke.

He laughs nicely: can you be in love with a voice? A disembodied relationship could be quite pleasant, an intercourse of voices... . We talk for about forty minutes, effortlessly: he is amazed not to have heard of Hilary Mantel; he himself wrote a book a long time ago, which took him everywhere in the world; it did quite well at the time. He asks where I live: North London, with a gorgeous garden, lots of trees, squirrels... . What about him? He has a flat in central London, on the river actually, and even sees whales...

He finally asks if I will have dinner with him, the week after next though, he has to attend a conference. That's fine with me.

It suddenly strikes me that his small ad, unlike so many others, doesn't ask for love, a long-term relationship, or a soul mate – but nor does it require as some others do, an 'uncomplicated' companion 'up for a laugh and an adventure'. He is unattached, he told me on the telephone, has no children or rather has two stepchildren, grown up by now – so he had married a divorced woman or a widow; it's sad he doesn't have children of his own, but this may be to my advantage: he is freer.

(It bothers me that, because of the strict definition of this undertaking – looking for love, a partner in life – the mind leaps ahead over so many steps, so many hurdles, it even imagines touching, having sex, going on holidays...)

At least he doesn't require I should be 'ultra slim'-nor 'a size eighteen' thank goodness! If he wanted 'small' he would probably be short himself unless he loved to dominate – or protect. An 'adventurer' on the same page is asking for 'statuesque, feminine, demure, classically elegant'…a tall order, but I have seen such women on Sunday afternoons, visiting art galleries, they amble gracefully across the rooms in easy self-containment, apparently unaware of others and accompanied by tall and distinguished-looking men, who would be architects, academics, writers maybe; how I envied them!

Ross is wise enough to require 'interesting and attractive': broad enough, reassuring. He may know that chemistry, physical and intellectual, is what really matters, it cuts across everything else: size, looks, origins. He may not look for love, merely good company, a relationship without ties. However, I believe I know what the single life, particularly in later years, truly requires. And since he loves Anita Brookner's books he is bound to be emotionally intelligent even if he is cautious. But can it be that he loves her novels because he identifies with the people she describes, their intelligent and resigned lonesomeness?

Can he 'do' affection? Can he touch? For I have known men who couldn't, or else only inappropriately…

These meandering thoughts and conjectures may be futile: if I had met Ross a day or two after Peter, not having much leisure, I would have given our meeting a lot less thought. Having time to think can be a profitable activity – unless it is merely a nefarious, neurotic endeavour. And all this because of his voice…

Naturally he will have had dinner with several women already, possibly more than once. It's good that he perseveres, as he shows by meeting me; only by being pragmatic would you allow for a discriminating choice eventually. I should do the same except that I haven't seen any other appealing small ads these last two weeks. He's at an advantage, having had many replies; has he earmarked one or two of his dinner dates for further exploration? Was he charmed by any of them? Did he feel desire? Many of them would be much younger than him, women being aware and often accepting of the usual equation; but also younger than I, fresher, sprightlier, more slender – different; of course they wouldn't be French, but what does it mean? The way I live these days, it cannot matter that I am French or anything else, I seem to be the prisoner of routines; some necessary – but to have my life reduced to these routines…I have recently caught sights of myself I'm appalled at. I cannot deny I enjoy going to supermarkets: that abundance, the impulse to choose, the reward of instant gratification. But confronting the other older women I meet mid-morning in those supermarkets, their own routines, I could see that I may be becoming as I imagine them in my dread; I had entered by mistake an enclosure for people not just beyond my years but possibly beyond hope. I was horrified: I was still so young, didn't you notice how young I look? How I walk? Did you know I dream of travels, love-making in the afternoon, riding horses in Arizona, learning how to fly aeroplanes? I am appalled at the creeping banality of some of my days, my isolation, I must have been exiled without my noticing. I should fight back, for having all this time to myself hardly feels like real freedom, more like an imposed holiday that I am meant to be grateful for. I can see that 'Real Life', if it is still there somewhere, has been placed in abeyance, and I have to deserve it now more than ever…for the alternative is that I will disappear.

I knew so well, as a child, how not to exist: Mother had taught me, time and again. Now, long after leaving childhood behind, I could still sense that the helplessness was there, like an old schoolfriend one has no wish to meet again but whose manners, words and company feel so familiar they are once more, at least for a while, dreadfully easy to merge with. An old looking-glass with a ghost in it.

Looking at myself was useful, revealing over the years a measure of the distance between being and having been. Now I am not so sure: the mirror is equivocal, at times a friend, at others a Judas, often unsettling. In its more precise moments it would reflect a face that still has most of its contours and is well defined mainly because of a very short haircut that suits a head of balanced proportions. The eyes are large, blue and lively – inquisitive, they also hide little. As a little girl I wanted to have Mum's eyes, which was uncertain as I grew up and my features kept altering subtly, seeking final definition, but you couldn't have wished for more beautiful eyes: large, soft and so blue, they were a blessing when accompanied by a smile, and a torment when they lapsed into wistfulness or disapproval. People would say I have her eyes but I know better: my eyelids aren't so well designed or so long, nor my eyebrows so round as suited her time and fashion.

My nose is too long for my liking, which caused me great distress and anguish as an adolescent, particularly if my sister, during our arguments, administered the mortal blow:

– You have a nose like Daddy's!

This was never true but threatened to be true for a long time, as young people know that their features haven't acquired their definitive shape, and hope for or dread a different look than the one they see in the mirror each anxious morning. My father had a 'Bourbon' nose, large and curved like those of ancient French kings. It gave gravitas and character to an otherwise bland face. To my sister and me it had become the mark of his appearance, and since we hated him for making Mum cry, 'the nose' became the evil trait. As I grew up, my own nose grew with me, to be balanced in my twenties by eventual cheekbones which made it more acceptable by accentuating my eyes.

My mouth is of average size and fleshy, much improved by lipstick. It knows how to laugh, shout, and kiss. It also knows how to eat, voluptuously. My chin is an odd thing, with seemingly a life of its own: apparently independent of my jaw, it can firm itself in stubbornness, or tremble emotionally.

My neck is becoming problematic: being self-conscious about it, I am acquiring a better posture, keeping my head straight when I can, an effort immediately undone by laughter, when I suddenly couldn't care less...

How will Ross look at me? What will he see? Will he like me? It is conceivable, though unlikely, that I will not like him much more than my previous date. I know, however, that we shall talk like friends, even if the possibility of friendship should elude us after that first dinner, as we each move on with our quest.

Chapter Four

The clematis by my sheltered front door decided some time ago to sprout lively buds and leaves, ignoring the stubbornness of winter. A ray of sun at the back illuminates the garden and I feel suddenly elated, as if given a bunch of flowers by an unexpected lover. It is a fact that we are now in spring.

It must have been spring too when Emmanuel came into my life six or seven years ago. His letter in reply to my small ad had been the nicest, the most well-rounded: a business lawyer temporarily working in Birmingham, he was planning an eventual move to London, to Hampstead actually. An Ashkenazy Jew, he was evidently educated, adored music, the arts, and was an 'avid reader'. The tone was self-assured without pomposity, there was simplicity and friendliness as well, which was attractive. He was fifty-four (to my nearly sixty), divorced, no children – 'no baggage'. The fact that he was French promised to compensate, if our relationship took shape, for my desperate craving for France: I had left it long ago in search for peace away from my family: this had been a high price to pay. I missed my country, my landscapes, my culture, and I remember bursting into tears each time I went across because it was then all mine again, for a short while.

It is Emmanuel's frenchness that sustained our initial relationship: for five whole weeks we spoke on the telephone, and if I was curious, interested even, he seemed ever hungrier for these long calls, which made me wonder why he didn't jump on the first train to London. Fear of failure may have been what stopped him, but in those five weeks we became close friends, which would eventually open other doors.

When I eventually met him at Euston station, I couldn't help an internal 'Oh my God!': a fat man, thankfully very tall, but fat. I immediately scolded myself: so what? He is your friend! Aware of my own concerns about my looks, I forbade myself such considerations in relation to others. Besides, I knew he was a good man.

I took in but chose to ignore his modest-looking jacket, dark green with few details, which obviously came from one of the cheaper large stores. The trousers were navy blue and good, the shirt indifferent. His bulk, however, he carried better than most because of being six foot-two and broad-shouldered, and I had to admit that it gave him an air of professional authority. Although his forehead had been getting larger in recent years, most of his black hair was still in evidence, with a tendency to curl. His eyes wore a severe look which could have stemmed in part from a feeling of anxiety: how would our meeting pan out? Five weeks of increasingly frequent telephone conversations had given our relationship a more urgent slant. 'I was afraid,' he confessed later, 'that you wouldn't like me.' For my part I was meeting a friend, my French friend, and was more well-disposed than was good for me, as it would turn out... . In spite of his lack of natural charm and dour appearance, Emmanuel knew the ropes.

The first thing we did was check in and leave his overnight bag at the hotel where I had reserved a room for him, then go for a late lunch at a nearby Greek restaurant. The conversation was friendly, and we were both relieved to wrap in physical reality the mere voices we had been to each other for so long. His manner of speech was slow and ponderous – he was a lawyer after all – but well-informed and intelligent: we were of the same country, the same culture, we had read some of the same books, had the same political references and equal interest in art. We had set out the map.

When we came out of the restaurant over two hours later, during which, having secretly felt a man again, Emmanuel decided I was 'a fine woman', he asked me to stop the car at a florist's: the huge bunch of sunflowers were for the house, he declared, and the single rose for me. I melted: these things were what mattered.

'Things' had gone very fast: I had found his company easy, he had found me attractive – 'sparkling', he had said – and we were both needy, with the added bond of our Frenchness in exile. It was only slowly, over the following weeks and months, that the crucial facts leaked out: he was not presently working but applying for his French qualifications to be recognised by the Law Society. His career had been interrupted by some heart problems, but he was now fine on medication. His mother was helping him financially as he was subsisting on benefits. And didn't I find him later living in a barely habitable ground floor council flat in Birmingham? That was after his cardiac accident, he explained, as he couldn't manage the stairs in the colleague's house where he occupied a room...

As these facts came out little by little, quietly, and we were already in a relationship where my loyalty and compassion had an increasing part to play, it was inconceivable that I could retrace my steps. Besides, hadn't I been brought up to place other people's needs before my own? The journey seemed inescapable in its familiarity.

All my hopes for a future came to a full stop when Emmanuel's health started to deteriorate after a short time. Listening to his breathing in bed was nightmarish, as he sometimes gasped, then was silent and still for what seemed like minutes at a time and I often wondered if I wouldn't wake up next to a corpse. The fact that he was on medication seemed a guarantee for a while, assuring us protection, but increasing shortness of breath, chaotic heartbeats and a few blackouts warned of worse to come. When the skin on his face began to go grey, I insisted – he had refused so far – that we go to my doctor who immediately sent him to hospital. He would remain there for three weeks for multiple tests, after which they would decide on new medication. I finally took home an improved man but the consultant had decreed his future: he was putting him on the waiting-list for a heart transplant at Harefield Hospital. We read up on transplants, their benefits and many drawbacks, their limits (five years' survival on average), the sacrifices we would have to make; the loss of his immune system would render him ever fragile; I was counselled to be 'understanding'. 'You will never work again,' they told him casually.

After a few weeks, Emmanuel's health deteriorated once more: he collapsed in the street, his breathing was haphazard and his complexion again went grey. We knew there was no hope; the new treatment hadn't worked, the damaged mitral valve was struggling desperately with a heart muscle that was giving up. In tears, we twice said goodbye to each other: he wouldn't make it to the transplant.

I then learnt through an acquaintance that a healer was working in my street, across the road as it happened. I am normally able and prompt to read the writing on the wall. But such a feeling as hope, halfway to belief, seemed too daring and required more commitment to life than I was able to make at the time: I waited two weeks. I had had to give up, during our first year together, everything I had hankered for, that a relationship with a normal man would have given me: a lasting partnership that would have been about mutual caring, reasonable prosperity, holidays in France and elsewhere; a career for him that would keep him independent of me. Instead of which everything rested on my shoulders added to my unwanted role as his nurse and nanny, his keeper: I was beginning to hate my life.

The spur of anger had become stronger than despair: I didn't 'do' resignation easily, action was the only path to take.

I contacted the healer. A maverick, Trond worked on Emmanuel carefully to start with, his hands at a distance, as he knew he could have killed him with the intensity of his power. I watched as Emmanuel, exhausted by the healing sessions, sank each time into heavy sleep. After a few treatments, his breathing was already better, but like the four-year old child he was, he wanted to stop seeing Trond: "He hurts me!" he cried. I replied I didn't care, he would carry on seeing Trond two or three times a week as long as he lived in my house. I could see what was happening: Emmanuel's cheeks had become pink again, blood flowing regularly to his brain, his speech and breathing were becoming more natural, there were no more blackouts.

A hospital appointment that had been scheduled months before for an endoscopy was due that February. Emmanuel had had nineteen sessions with Trond by then. The doctor who had just performed the procedure looked at me as if I was a complete fool when I asked if Emmanuel had any hope of avoiding a heart transplant:

– A heart transplant? Where on earth did you get that idea?

I gave him the name of the consultant on the third floor.

– Well, I insisted, what about the mitral valve? Is it now operable?

– There is hardly anything wrong with the mitral valve, he snapped contemptuously.

I had never been so proud to be thought stupid by anyone: the healing had worked.

*

We carried on with healing sessions once a week if only to reinforce the benefits already acquired. I had healing too, and some of my strength came back, with some equanimity. This I badly needed, for our relationship had foundered. I had been living with a man totally incapable of affection, albeit a sweet companion. Emmanuel, thrilled at his newly acquired energy – relative, for he didn't dare give up the several drugs that made him impotent, among other side effects – decided he would resume his career from home.

The telephone rang constantly and he soon needed a laptop – a good one – a fax machine, a printer; headed writing paper. Appointments were made with important business contacts for which he needed good suits, a coat, a smart briefcase, and money to pay for drinks and food in good restaurants; and air fares, and hotel bills. In the house, the living room had become his office, faxes arriving several times a day from oil companies and various trading outfits, banks, and newly contacted ex-trading partners. I was introduced to the speculative world of wheeling and dealing in commodities of all kinds, but mostly in oil. The commissions, tiny in percentage terms, added up to extraordinary sums. There was nothing to disbelieve, I could read the faxes, the contracts, witness the telephone conversations with people in Moscow, Venezuela, Azerbadjan, the Congo, the United Arab Emirates, Australia…

I also learned about hope gone mad, illusion, crushing disappointments. I could see Emmanuel's work capability, it was quite impressive. ('You will never work again,' the doctors had told him. They now congratulated themselves on his good recovery, having scoffed at my mention of the healer.)

But I could also see in Emmanuel a hunger so overwhelming he confused it at times with power: he was now so strong he would become so successful, SO RICH. His hunger wasn't confined to riches: it had manifested itself from the start by a hunger for food that promptly led me to giving him a salad bowl for his portions of pasta, meat stews; I had to restrict him to half a chicken at a time. Our expeditions to the supermarket were the ruin of me and I eventually decided to shop alone. I was getting broke, and if I wasn't careful, I would end up myself, like a fish bone on the side of his plate.

I started to express my impatience. 'Throw him out!' said my friends. I didn't feel one could throw a human being out onto the pavement, for Emmanuel it would mean going back on benefits and the end of his hopes – and I would never be repaid. For I had by then spent practically all my savings, several dozens of thousands of pounds, not to mention part of my pension fund. He assured me success was now very close.

He had also renewed contact with an ex-girl-friend, someone he had known while studying at Law School, and Sylvia had invited him to Corsica where she lived for a holiday: would I mind lending him the fare? It occurred to me that I could do with a holiday myself;

however, the prospect of a fortnight (the latest contract wouldn't take much longer to come through) without him would be a welcome rest. I also felt, as he constantly assured me, that I could count on his gratitude, he would compensate me many times over, and I already had several signed and dated acknowledgements confirming his intentions.

When Emmanuel returned at the end of July, suntanned and looking happy, I knew what had happened, confirmed by a large number of letters arriving daily from Corsica, and mounting telephone bills, for he would never hesitate to use his mobile to talk to her for hours on end despite my pleas. He worked harder than ever on a new contract, the previous one, like so many others, having failed.

– I want you to leave, I said in September.

– It won't be long, he assured me in November.

– It's all done now, the contracts have been signed, he announced in early December. If he was exhausted by his efforts, I was drained of all hope, patience and tolerance.

– You look tired, I said mid-December, you need a holiday. How about I buy you a single air fare to Corsica and you can come and collect your things when your money comes through after Christmas?

He couldn't believe his luck. Neither could I, and I drove him to the airport to make sure he was truly on his way.

He never came back. That was over five years ago now, and Sylvia will have had to show patience and forbearance, as I had. He may still be working at making his fortune. And she may have learnt that he has no scruples.

*

It took me ages to recover from the damage. Financially, I was ruined and had to sell my house; this was mitigated by the fact that I badly wanted to leave my Camden Town neighbourhood behind. My reduced circumstances gave me little hope of finding something suitable in a better area, but an old friend died and what he left me helped greatly: I could downsize and upgrade at the same time, and found a small garden flat further up the hill which provided me with what I needed: calm, beauty, and safety. Emotionally, relieved as I was at Emmanuel's departure, all the efforts I had made towards our relationship, then his survival, then his professional success, left me worn out: I felt like an empty shell and wished for nothing but peace of mind and rest. I would be drawing a line under relationships, for ever probably, I couldn't envisage even yearning again.

*

If the wound isn't entirely deadly, we tend to heal, don't we? The scars are there, but the blood flows still. After a few years of what some would call convalescence, I needed and wanted to love again. Although I didn't feel I had truly loved Emmanuel, we had got on well, like a couple of sorts, necessary to each other, for a while. And I can see more clearly now how mercilessly he exploited me. I never heard of him again, a relief of sorts, and of course never got any money back. I know that, regardless of his feelings for her, if Sylvia still has some money, he'll be sharing with her that little Corsican paradise.

Chapter Five

Ross, my 'dinner companion', hasn't rung yet, and probably won't. 'It won't be next week,' he had said, 'because I have a conference, but the week after.' Well, the week after has passed; I figured he had a huge report to write. He is a busy man, an active man.

This morning, I startled myself with the thought that he had possibly forgotten about me – but we had talked for about forty minutes, about books, his journeys, all kind of things, and he asked if I would have dinner with him! I would go just to hear his voice again: mellifluous, I would have called it. It had made me feel quite dreamy.

The newly arrived spring has transformed the garden, the sun alone seems to promise impossible things, and I could weep already at my inevitable disappointment. What sap I have left still rises, risks choking me at times, like a rush of petrol in an old engine. But I feel fulfilled standing in the sun, as if a loved man was taking my arm. (I remember that old photographer – actually, he was my age – who took my arm after dinner once, the warmth of it, that temporary togetherness had almost made me gasp, then the transience of it.)

What a coincidence it had been, Ross trying to call

me at the precise moment I was leaving him a new message: he had expressed astonishment at the synchronicity. I am not so surprised since he mentioned in his spoken message that he is a Taurean. I get on very well with Taureans: Emmanuel was a Taurean, so is my daughter's boyfriend. He asked what job my daughter did, and I told him – with so much praise for her talents that I heard him smile: an indulgent, kind smile.

Something he said in his ad had struck me: the word 'irony'. He declared himself 'interested in human nature, conversation and irony'. Why irony? It is not quite the same as humour, it is further on, slightly close to sarcasm when used on others. Is it philosophical irony? The distance we place between our hopes and an unreliable outcome? The way we shade our expectations once we have learned about failure? I hope he is not caustic; 'caustic' is unfriendly, corrosive even; while there is connivance in humour. Did he simply want to differentiate himself from nearly everyone else who asks for GSOH?

We could talk about all that...

I had an ironic day yesterday – no, humorous, like a joke I played on myself, albeit after the fact: the sun was shining, lifting me into such a state of sheer joy that I decided to go to a department store and browse at the summer clothes. (The red skirt I bought last month had been a loud and at the time unconscious precursor to the adventure I was to undertake.) I could even let in a little hope as a side effect of the nascent spring.

Strolling in the aisles, letting colours guide me, I finally stopped in front of two skirts: one was multicoloured in creased Indian silk, long and shimmering: it spoke of a rejuvenated me, happy as I only hoped to be in my dreams, strolling in a sunny French village, holding hands with a loving man. The other one was equally fabulous, with large flowers of turquoise and blue on a light grey background. (He would say: 'This one is superb with your eyes!') Unable to decide, I bought them both. The moment I left the store, I started chuckling, knowing that I would return them the next day, particularly if the weather turned cloudy, but it was nice to own them for a day, innocent hostages to my spring madness.

Spring doesn't just affect me. What old dogs were sleeping now show a spark in their eyes, like that silly man I sometimes see on my way to the shops who makes little owl noises as he passes me. Highly irritating, not necessarily flattering, but there had been that young actor I saw last week at the supermarket and who gave me the eye. I was surprised, but it is true to say that my own eyes haven't gone dull.... Some people seem to suffer from permanent cataracts, and I think I know why: so many are simply broken, broken by life. It may just depend on what stage you have reached, what capital of health, looks, mental faculties and aspirations you still possess and nurture. A new endeavour can represent an act of hope over experience; it can also be an effort of will over despair, as I occasionally suspect is my case. Simple joy, of course, would abolish all obstacles, let the sun shine in regardless of season.

Talking with Ross on the telephone about Anita Brookner has led me to read once more: *Undue Influence*. I enjoyed it, although with occasional impatience at the minutiae. A sentence remains with me, though: **"...she had thought to do without love, only to be shown that love was on offer to those who knew how to deal with it."**

If the criterion for 'knowing how to deal with it' is that you must have experienced true love in childhood – unconditional, attentive, joyous – then I would, had I remained who I was born to be, prove a complete failure. People who claim to have 'no baggage' don't know what they are talking about. They merely mean: no wife or husband, no children, no wooden leg, nothing that shows. But if we have come to realise that we learn soon after birth and throughout our childhood the principles of love inherent to our family, then we come to that first meeting with a potential mate laden with unseen gifts or crippled with incompleteness if not seeping wounds.

For my mother, love was imbued with need; for my father, it seemed a distant attachment of sorts, he didn't seem too sure and soon came to spoil it. My sister and I learnt, practically from the breast, that 'love' is needy, anxious, conditional, demanding and finite. I came to understand that the kind of loving I had learnt was possibly crippling and abhorrent to others, because it was incoherent, damaged, and consequently harmful. Hence a rich history of wrong choices and heartaches. I got a great deal better over the decades, though. I have also learnt that I musn't necessarily sacrifice my well-being to others'.

I never used to think I had a right to be happy, so much did childhood feel like a slow death. Happiness always seemed such a fleeting grace, something granted rather than acquired, even less deserved. Aware of the haphazardness of its delivery, my aims were elsewhere, and although I certainly sought love out, I never really assumed it should make me happy. Examples were everywhere. I knew from books what real life could be like; I thought I knew. In my early teens, having read Jack London, love took the shape of a tall man in a lumberjack shirt standing in the doorway of our humble abode, after a day's hunting, crowned by the light behind him. Childhood planted inaccessible dreams in my head: between father, who was sad in a quiet but stern way and mother's poorly buried anger, the anxiety of growing up was placated by books and a friendly teacher's support. Among the vignettes in my head, I still have a vivid memory of that glorious young couple: I used to lean at our kitchen window, staring out at the road outside our house for signs of another life, and I often saw them, cycling side by side, his arm always around her waist or shoulders, smiling, chatting, him with his dark wavy hair and her with her sweet blue eyes and shoulder length blond curls. They seemed to have a halo around them. The image left me disconcerted, wistful. Another is of my mother coming home one afternoon, having had tea with a new acquaintance, the wife of a writer who had a house in the hills nearby. She came back excited, at once elated and thoughtful: 'Do you know what she told me about her husband? "He is my friend, my son, my brother and my lover.." Isn't that wonderful? It's the most beautiful thing...' She was silent after that. May be it was just for other people...

In the middle of my own fumblings with love, I watched others for guidance at times, at other times with foreboding: I knew a woman once, whose story is to me a cautionary tale, so much did her way of loving betray her neediness: Colette was her name, an attractive woman of undisguised sexuality in her early forties, always dressed in feminine clothes. She was kind too, bringing me some soup one day when I was ill. She sometimes came to tea and we talked a great deal, of our lives, our hopes. She had grown up, as was not infrequent in our days, between a passive mother and an inaccessible father, with a resultant lack of self-esteem. You would have known who she was by merely stepping into her house: an artist's studio with high ceilings, skylight and beams, she had turned it into an altar to love: the photo frames, pictures, mirrors and diverse objects large and small were all in the shape of hearts, acting out (but I doubt it was unconscious) her need and hopes. She was pining for the love of Anthony, a musician she had known a long time, and with whom she had had a liaison several years beforehand when she and her husband were close friends with him and his wife. Their affair had put an end to her marriage, and Anthony had left his wife so he and Colette could at last be together. This is when Anthony's wife became ill with breast cancer. Judging he could no longer leave her alone in that state, Anthony went back to her and looked after her devotedly until she died. Colette begged him to come to her afterwards, but he must have felt responsible for his wife's illness and death: for two years he hesitated, in turns appearing to give in and then changing his mind. These were the years I knew Colette. She was crushed by his indecision: happiness seemed so close, yet elusive. She met him frequently when he was back in London after his travels, anxious beforehand and desperate afterwards, obsessed with his conquest: nothing else seemed to exist, she wanted Anthony, she could only be happy with him, she would have no peace till he came to her, but as none of her arguments and her entreaties seemed to convince him, she retreated into despair:

– If only I could get breast cancer, I know he would come to me then! she exclaimed in frustration one day.

Months passed and Colette fell ill with breast cancer. She didn't look too frightened, it seemed she was conducting her destiny with dark determination. Anthony, whom she saw often now, still prevaricated. While she went through a mastectomy and spoke to me of her plans for reconstructive surgery, she also raged about him:

– I know the kind of man he is! He is the sort who gives cancer to women!

I never could stand delusion, illusion, lies or connivance, and felt I was bringing her back to the truth when I reminded her that she had wished all this upon herself. As a result, she never saw me again. However, two years later, visiting a dressmaker whom she had recommended to me in the past, I asked about Colette:

– Oh, dear, you don't know, said the woman.

Colette and Anthony were due to be married just two months previously. She had made all of Colette's clothes for the occasion, the going-away outfits. Anthony didn't show up for the ceremony, having run away abroad. She had recently heard that Colette had fallen seriously ill.

*

I had my hair cut a few days ago, which always makes me feel renewed, ready for something. It is another routine, a necessary one: I like to look good, well-groomed; it inevitably leaves me with a feeling of expectation: where shall I go? What shall I do?

Lucy cuts my hair at home and has been coming for years; I hate salons. It is all done very quickly, and as we talk, we each know the familiar references as she has done my hair for over twenty-six years. She is herself a beautiful and bright person, a good person. I talk to her about ageing sometimes, but she knows, she watches closely, from above, her eye keen. She said to me two years ago:

– Your eyelids haven't fallen yet.

She couldn't say that now: the left one is definitely weakening, the skin coming away from its socket. That's how it goes, it is insidious, sly, treacherous, awful. It is also laughable, in a sad way, as there is no escape. Of course, one could die while still looking good, before the disasters, but I am no longer a romantic, and it is too late to die young...

*

Ross hasn't rung yet. I imagine papers on his table, with a small crowd of telephone numbers. He is confused: which one is which? He had thought he would remember but doesn't, and cannot risk ringing again by mistake such or such woman he had not liked. He should have been more organised, which one is Hélène's?

Does he know how to 'deal with' love? Just because he is well-spoken, cultured, fluent, doesn't mean he is any better at relationships than many of us; this will all depend on whether he has been well-loved as a child, and therefore thinks well of himself. 'Cambridge educated' is double-edged, I know. I know the type. His parents will probably have been affluent and sent him to board early, at the age of eight. They may have thought this would be best for him, not realising what an emotional cripple he would turn out to be, much like themselves – shy of his feelings, afraid to show them, incapable of affection except five minutes before sex. That's why he doesn't seek outright 'a woman to love and be loved by', but, cautiously, a 'dinner companion'... . I speculate in a vacuum, if we do not meet I will never know... . He is the man without a face. Living at once in Central London and on the river sounds wonderful, and since I live in Belsize Park with a gorgeous garden, we could easily to and fro; ideal, really (neither of us is giving up our flat, we have agreed on some independence; we meet often, always at weekends, and plan holidays in France, we might even buy a place there...).

I think about him a lot, he has almost become a part of my life, being almost material at times, so that when we finally meet, there may be a third person sitting with us at the table, maybe superimposed, maybe watching, smiling indulgently.

Chapter Six

I can see through the window the garden smiling under the early sun, preparing itself for its blue period. There is still yellow about – the small daffodils, varied, full of liveliness in their apparent disorder; the pink and white hellebores, which were late and therefore will stay a while, stand reliably in clumps. Their delicacy is hidden: you have to lift the bloom as you would hold up the chin of a small child to better look into his eyes, in order to see the concealed preciousness, the beauty spots, the slight streaks of crimson. The blues are late this spring; I have planned some – the upright grapes of the muscari, the ceanothus – and allowed the others, the delinquent forget-me-nots peppering every available space, even creeping onto the lawn, and particularly the bluebells which I inherited and do not like to discipline too much…everything seems immersed in the excitement of growing and the vagaries of the season are coming off on me – the impatience, the need to thrive. Hurry up, I want to show you my garden in bloom!

I should go back to the gym, I haven't been for at least two months. I used to go regularly, three times a week in the mornings for seven months, then back home feeling better and dutiful, ready for the day. Over the last weeks,

I had started skipping some exercises, giving up on some machines, leaving earlier and earlier. On the last day, I was sitting on a bench to get my breath back after a bout on the treadmill, when one of the trainers I knew by sight stopped by and asked how I was doing.

– Not terrific, I said, I am slowing down, feeling a bit low I guess...

– Let me give you a session and we'll go over your programme, he said with a smile, I won't charge you, and it'll help you get back into it.

– Why would you do it for no money? I asked, disbelieving.

– Well, it's not all about money, is it? If it helps you...

– OK, I said, near tears, you're incredibly kind...

He gave me his name and went, and I started to weep quietly. A couple of women stopped by to ask if I was all right. I went home soon after. I didn't know I was feeling so alone.

But I should go back. It was good for me, and I could firm up a stomach seemingly attracted by the lure of gravity. Down with gravity!

*

This will be my last effort, before I move on to other pastures: I shall leave another message for Ross. Of course I won't even know for sure that he will know about it, he might have stopped listening to his voicemail some time ago, so I will leave this in the hands of fate (it likes it that way...) I may be persistent, possibly, but not desperate: this I will show by being ironic, which he claims to love. Something like:

"Hello, Ross, it's Hélène here, the person who spoke to you about Hilary Mantel's books. You haven't rung me back and it crosses my mind you may have lost my number

– or confused it with someone else's? Now, I don't want to deprive you of the opportunity to make contact again should you wish to do so: it would be nice, and you had mentioned dinner after all.

"If you have met someone you like, of course it would be superfluous, except that a call to explain this would be polite as well as interesting, and show me that these things do happen, giving some hope.

"If you don't ring me, however, I will assume that you have died of bird flu or something, and therefore will not call again."

It seems as if I have said goodbye and I feel free now, there are plenty more fish in the sea… . Tired fish, hungry fish.

*

> – LAWYER, 60, 6'2. Average build. Cultured, caring, easy-going, warm, romantic, WLTM attractive warm lady for friendship and LTR.

Haven't I had enough of lawyers with Emmanuel? – and my own father?

'Average build' may mean he is a little rotund (so he will not mind my size 14). The rest sounds nice: cultured, caring, warm. A sense of humour is required, though – even irony! I can't be doing with too conventional a man, I've had enough of that as a child…

> – PROFESSIONAL MALE, 61, easy-going, caring, loving, GSOH, into films, theatre, holidays, eating out, golf, skiing, would like to meet a lady with similar interests for LTR. London.

This man doesn't say 'educated' or 'cultured', but he

likes all the right things. I think I know who he is: a good, reliable, middle class man; husband material; (but I do not necessarily require a husband). Golf is very good, he can go on his own and I can do my own thing; one of my friends loves her husband to play golf, she would go mad otherwise, she says.

Yes, I know, they are younger than me, but many men seem to age fast and I would want more of a future for mine. Besides, I am still young in looks and attitude, and they are under no obligation to have me! These two small ads are from two Sundays ago and were left in abeyance because I was expecting Ross's call...

I brace myself to reply. If it is easy enough to feel detached from 'the exercise' when not engaged in it, it seems that my hesitations to resume it betray an anxiety I have been too prompt to dismiss. This is serious. And hadn't I better write my reply down so as not to forget any detail I would like to mention? It limits spontaneity but would save me from repeating myself.

"My name is Hélène. I am in my mid-fifties, attractive, young-looking, and confident. I am lively with an inquisitive mind and am a Radio 4 listener. I was born and brought up in France where I attended university. I am looking for a man of broad culture who is, like me, interested in people and ideas. I often visit art galleries and I love books, films and the theatre. I also write.

I live in a nice area of North London, where I enjoy a beautiful garden. I love gardening and nature generally, and would love to travel more.

Over the years I have worked as a teacher, a counsellor and an interior designer. Conversation is one of my favourite pastimes. So it would be great to have a friendly conversation with a man of 55 to 62 years who is fit, active, intelligent, solvent, kind and thoughtful, with a view to a lasting relationship. A sense of humour is a must. My telephone number is…"

It is, on reading it, a little disorganised, but it will do.

*

The lawyer is divorced with two grown-up children. He had his own business and now works as a consultant as and when he likes. He lives near Hampstead in a house which actually has roses growing on the front. He loves reading, and has dabbled in writing. He relishes good conversation, attended a philosophy course some time ago, enjoys board games, like chess, etc. and to watch sport as well as going out to fringe theatres, the cinema. He likes eating in good company. He is easy-going, supportive, has a good sense of humour and is tactile. He would love a special friend, warm, attractive, for a long-term relationship.

I am quite moved: this is a good man, who somehow comes across as a complete human being, a man of good will. The voice helps, warm and self-assured. I shall ring him, after I have listened to the message of the second man.

The 'Professional male' is an architect, divorced with two grown-up children. He lives in Bromley, describes himself as caring and loving. He is looking for a long-term relationship with a lady of the same tastes to do most things with: go to the theatre, films, holidays, etc. His message is surprisingly short which initially leads me to think he may have little to say – of course he may be intimidated by what he is doing, it might be the first time…. . However, this message lacks strength, or he may be weakened by his need. I shall not reply.

I feel emotionally exhausted: communicating in this manner may all seem quite abstract because we have never set eyes on each other, but the declared intent of our undertaking somehow lays us bare, vulnerable. So I go on a long walk to Primrose Hill to get my balance back: the afternoon sun is now casting long shadows and the wind is brisk. Good.

*

I have a postcard of an angel on my desk, with clear glass around it like a halo. It's only got one wing; these things happen to angels too, I still feel lopsided without mine, but there you go…life…I used to say: No! This is not LIFE! indignant, as I wanted more, better, fuller… . Well, there it goes. The flow is too strong to resist at times and you find yourself clinging to debris, branches, you struggle to reach a bank.

I need a safe beach. Where I can hold hands with a man and feel: yes, this is right, this is good, and be at peace. Home.

*

I am a child, and Mother is cooking; Father will be back from work soon. He has expectations of his dinner on the table, his wife at heel, his daughters compliant. The food will be good, even a simple omelette will be perfect, it is a must. 'I don't want him to be able to reproach me for anything!' she protests. She says 'him' because she is speaking to herself about her husband, otherwise she would say: 'your father' …

Later, sitting behind my parents at the back of our car, I would invent a young man – we loved each other – who would come to release me or at least sit next to me a while; I would put my head inside his coat, against his heart. Later still, I would howl dark existential songs by Jean-Paul Sartre about living in deprived tenements where the sun never shone and there was no hope. Father would drive on, locked inside his own walls. Surprisingly, mother never asked me to stop: it was still singing, for heaven's sake, better than screaming.

As I grew up, there was light relief at times, but I could never properly read the script and life doesn't forgive you for that.

Chapter Seven

I've had no call from 'the lawyer' over the weekend, which concerns me slightly. Of course his ad appeared nearly two weeks before I replied and he will have had a lot of messages to go through, will have had dates with several women, so much to occupy his mind that he may not think to listen to his voice box again, where my message is languishing. And all that because I was waiting for Ross to call back as arranged and fix our dinner date. I haven't been very business-like in my enterprise, which is bound to fail if I start forming attachments the moment I hear a moving voice. The weekend papers didn't offer many – if any – personal ads that spoke to me. Yet I got distracted reading them all, marvelling at the diversity: two men describe themselves as very handsome and two more as 'lovely': some people just love themselves, which must help I suppose, since they would be convincing. Danger lurks with a self-declared 'ANGRY MAN', who 'values intelligence, reasonableness and fairness' – and the Gods help you if you have none of these attributes! A 'Christian Poet' seeks a 'tall white Christian lady, vegetarian, 58-70, cat lover, not into sport, dancing, pubs, trousers or jeans', so a few negatives make a positive. Yet another calls himself 'cultural' when he obviously means 'cultured' – sorry, I'm a stickler for these things...

Most of the people in my age bracket are ordinary, run-of-the-mill bourgeois, conventional men – but then, how extraordinary am I? Not very, but I do not think I am boring; I have earned my place away from the so-dull, so-predictable, so-timorous world I grew up in. My father's exhortations to aim for 'the happy medium' (I thought it was something you fell into) were sure-fire recipes for remaining within his mediocrity and there was nothing I loathed more, for I had read dangerous books at a tender age: Jack London's adventure stories told me of wider horizons and bigger worlds where one had to fight not just for survival but one's principles; they allowed me, over the years, a radical outlook on my development. Oh, the battles... . For I also had to distance myself from my mother's adamant persuasion that my existence was merely tangential and dependent on hers, therefore unnecessary. Remaining inside her net meant being shaped by everlasting need and subservience. You cannot, however, call any odd attachment love. It grew increasingly important that proper, healthy loving should become possible in the future. I only had my books and my failures to rely on for my development, allied to a stubborn and salutary tendency to analyse. Have I made the grade now? And can I – may I? – find a partner endowed with some depth and understanding?

A friend of mine said to me some years ago – and it fixed itself in my mind like a revelation – that we generally do not love, as adults, any differently from the way we loved and were loved (or were dealt with) in childhood: the patterns of adult love are no different, in that we only ever express ourselves as we are – as we have been made, if we don't learn any better...I think I've learned better.

I may have lost some of the ability to endure relentless hardship, Emmanuel cured me of that, which may mean I am no longer as generous and selfless as I was, but more aware of my own worth, more determined to enjoy my fair share – determined that there should be joy.

*

I had a dream last night which is still sticking to me like old glue. I was due to fly to the US and found myself at the airport about to buy my ticket, only suddenly to forget the name of the town I was supposed to fly to. Overwhelmed with frustration and anxiety, I could only stammer: 'It is…it is…oh, I know it so well…you know… . If you have a map I'll show you, it'll come back to me in a minute' – and couldn't bear it because it didn't, and there was no map, only a queue of people behind me getting longer. How could I reach my destination if I couldn't even name it? I still felt that sense of being utterly lost without that knowledge, that certainty, that one name that would get me where I wanted to be, and the panic and distress to be so let down by myself.

Some dreams seem to demand that you should wake up and wash quickly – can I wash the inside of my brain?

The day limped clumsily along, sustained by the ungiving discipline of daily tasks. I lived it head down, stubbornly, thinking of what I must do, how I must do it, to be a woman who knows "how to deal with it": IT: Love: Loving. Like the woman I met each week at a poetry workshop whose poems were a celebration of her life with their lyrical and joyous tone. She was in her fifties, not especially attractive except for her enthusiasm (so I didn't have to be pretty myself, or young, to be happy?). I tried to make contact, hoping, I imagined, that if we became friends some of her joy would come off on me, would somehow contaminate me. Sharing a cup of tea at break time, she told me that her lover was an illustrator of children books, they had started living together a year previously; she had never been so happy in her life, and, no, she couldn't have a drink with me after the workshop as she would be rushing to him with French bread and Italian wine for their regular evening feast. She would remain a woman I would only be able to marvel at, the person almost opposite me in our half-circle, who wrote about blissful bodies and singing hearts, and I would be wondering how it was done, imagining embraces, laughter, as if I was watching through a glass wall, allowing me to see but not to touch, never to reach.

I spy, with my little eye...my divorced friend who now has a new man: we sat on either side of him in the cinema the other night, and I saw him confidently slip his arm under hers and clasp her hand, which she playfully slapped, and they exchanged slaps and pats for a while before settling down. I liked that. I watched him as we were having a drink afterwards, marvelling at how 'other' other people can be: his newness was almost shocking to me, so odd his skin, mouth, expressions, manners; of course he was now familiar to her, maybe it was just my reaction to his closeness to her which I couldn't imagine for myself and defended myself against. I think that way even more when I read ads from men promising sensual intimacy and I feel like saying: don't say that, it's out of place, insensitive, rude almost and I estrange myself, feeling cold and defensive against this imposition of premature familiarity. I exclude those men outright. But then, that's just me.

This weekend's crop of personal ads is disappointing; so many are similar to the point of being interchangeable, often unimaginative, reflecting banal, conventional people: who doesn't like good food and wine, going to films and plays? Give me con-ver-sa-tion! (I note that the 'Christian Poet' is advertising again and has added to his list of 'must not be into' the word: 'grandchildren'...) This time the nice ones are in Cheshire, West Wales, or Glasgow – why make it so difficult? At the same time as I feel I must find one or two men to reply to, if only for the sake of feeling pro-active, I scold myself for being too demanding, too fussy ('Lower your standards!' an ex-lover had advised. 'That's not what they are for!' I had retorted. I haven't changed.)

> – LATE 60s SEMI-RETIRED PROFESSIONAL, tall, intelligent, cerebral and sensual, WLTM slim but slightly younger F. with whom to share life's pleasures.

I am not enthusiastic: there's nothing really wrong with him but he is too old. Why does he want a 'slightly younger' woman? Apart from the obvious –younger flesh – that's in order to have the upper hand, to be the senior and better partner, wiser, dominant. While I want a younger man because I look and act young and, in theory, a younger man will last longer, men are such fragile things, they can wilt or break: Emmanuel, six years my junior, had been a case in point, collapsing with heart failure a few months after moving in with me, his relative youth not even a guarantee...

> – MATURE LADY SOUGHT by professional gentleman, 53, for fun, friendship, relationship, companionship, possibly leading to more. I have many interests and am open to new ideas. Please call and I will reply.

I am intrigued: if he likes older women, I won't even

have to lie. However, he doesn't say who he is, only what he wants, and he is vague about his interests: is he hiding? Having prevaricated long enough, I decide to ring them both.

I am taken aback by the first one's attitude, whose name is Patrick: 'I am not going to repeat my ad,' he declares 'but voices are important, aren't they?' And without offering anything further about himself, he concludes: 'Now, let me hear yours.'

I feel frustrated and angry: I've had to listen to him without learning a single thing about his character or tastes: this man is immature, repressed, hides and plays tricks, and is probably incapable of intimacy. I grudgingly volunteer a few things about myself when I reply, why should I try to impress that idiot? I add in conclusion, testily: 'It's not just the voice one wants to hear, Patrick, but what that voice has to say, and you have nothing to say...'

The second one, for all his youth (he is fifty-three) has an elderly, staid, voice, and after repeating most of his ad, goes on to say that it is addressed to 'all sorts of ladies, even those who are not very mobile'. I imagine a one-man charity pushing old ladies in wheelchairs to the shops. What is worse, I imagine myself in a wheelchair, impotent, being pushed willy-nilly by a well-meaning fool, and I want to scream and kick and swear...

The friend I ring that evening to confide and moan about my calamitous attempts merely roars with laughter and explains that there are men with such fetishes who love their sex objects to be incapacitated, so they can be totally dominant, in kindness or in cruelty. I am horrified, but her husband teases me, commenting that it's merely a fetish I don't like, there would be others...

I sink into despondency: nothing will work, I shall never meet anyone decent, bright and kind. Although it is entertaining to note that two personal ads on that same page declare: 'Mrs Robinson wanted, by attractive 38 year-old male. Should be sexy, open-minded with GSOH', and 'Mrs Robinson required by cheeky, attractive man, 39', which could open horizons if I merely wished to play; it is also puzzling to read about that 'Non-atheist writer-artist, committed to: 1/ Eros; 2/ Wilderness; 3/ Eco-collapse and looking after ourselves,' to which he adds, quite logically, 'You can engage with Romans 12.2.'

I feel like closing the curtains, pulling the blinds down and locking the door. Going to bed. Sleeping. Forgetting. Not even remembering that there are things to forget. After a day and a night of mourning, knowing that I have been quite short with the 'semi-retired professional', who will have been offended and therefore not call me – which doesn't matter since he is an idiot anyway – I conclude I'll have to put in my own ad and ask for letters only: I will be better placed to choose among the multitude...

Chapter Eight

I know that when I think of love it is often with the eyes of the child. If we were merely, at birth, 'tabula rasa', I could well have ended up, aged twenty, say, as minus something (they had ways with education). Fortunately, there is something carried by blood maybe, flowing unstoppably, a hard desire to grow and thrive that sometimes likes to say 'no'. Of course it says 'yes' inappropriately, it hasn't yet learnt.

It isn't difficult remembering these things, they cling to you like shells to the rock face. The insistent long-term memory, selective, makes a point of leaving those traces, though possibly it cannot help it.

At the family table my parents seldom talked. He was a slim man, not tall, always well and formally dressed: as a lawyer, a small pillar of our starved provincial society, he had to play the part, and he knew no other. She used to be incredibly beautiful, then less so, and sadder still when he forbade her to dye her hair. She got heavier, walked with measured dignity, not always easy on our small town's inhospitable pavements. She was, reluctantly, a perfect housewife; however, because she had a gift for elegance, we lived in aesthetically pleasing surroundings: good if stiff antique furniture, pretty rugs, old engravings of town and country scenes, a couple of bronzes, some crystal vases, and large and light-hungry mirrors with golden frames. I often looked in them to make sure I was really there.

They hardly touched each other, at least not if she could help it, and he seldom dared. Except at night sometimes, though my sister and I never heard it, but it made her cry and he would stop the housekeeping money.

When their friends visited, our world was transformed: not that my parents always lied but they were relieved to be able to shed the tension between them and play happy. Few people knew; they came to play bridge, or to dinner, or both. The table was dressed beautifully and the food was wonderful. We had a help, who would wear a starched white pinafore with lace around the edges when she served at the table, then leave after doing the washing-up. My parents' friends were mostly couples, though there was a widow, a warm and bright Jewish lady who was my mother's best friend and very kind to my sister and me. Everyone liked her. There was the notary, a quiet fat man with a benevolent nature and his very entertaining wife: spirited and friendly, she made us all laugh although my mother, while enjoying her jokes, would deplore her vulgarity. Her husband spoiled her and she was grateful. There was the doctor (ears, nose and throat) and his elegant and reserved wife. They adored each other, a curiosity ('yes, my love', 'as you like, my darling'). I observed in awe. There was also a doddery old marechal – he was in his eighties – with a wife thirty years his junior who surprised my mother one day (and me, but they didn't know I could hear) '...and do you know what he wanted?? Yes, my dear!!!' I didn't know quite what they meant but imagined that it was rude.

On the family side I remember my Aunt Simone – my mother's sister – crushing a whole cream cake on her husband's face one lunch time and my uncle, totally non-plussed, continuing his conversation while wiping himself with his napkin. 'He had irritated her,' explained my mother when we got home. But years later, I heard my aunt complaining – vulgarly I thought – that 'I'm fed up of being screwed all the time!' My mother, who no longer had that problem, may have felt lucky for once.

My sweet and proper godmother lived with her husband in a large apartment in Bordeaux where we visited them regularly: he was her first cousin, and the story goes that, having survived the First World War, (he came back minus one eye), he told her: 'You won't escape from me now!' She wasn't able to resist his will. They lost their first baby and tried, unsuccessfully, for a second. He asked me once, leeringly, if I knew what people did when they wanted to have a child; I said yes, and my godmother protested shyly:

– Oh, Daniel, I'm ashamed…

*

The first time I experienced what can only be called love was the moment – was I nine or ten years old? – when our eyes met and the world metamorphosed: I was overwhelmed and, it seemed, so was he. We were transformed: it was a timid passion, private and solitary mostly, that we were only capable of expressing in glances where we lost ourselves. His name was Jeannot Roletti and his dad worked at the swimming pool.

In the Catholic Church's equivalent of the Girl Guides, I had found myself, a 'Valiant Soul', obediently doing what I was told by our supervisors. I remember a lot of walking up hills in rows, or standing, again in rows, singing hymns or listening to some speech or sermon. Jeannot was a 'Valiant Heart'. Our regiments, as they seemed, would occasionally share a hall, a church, but not mix. We never spoke, but I must have confided in another girl since I learned his name, and also that he wished to become a priest. All right, I thought, I would become a nun so we could be together. I cannot recall ever experiencing anything so strong in its purity, its uniqueness. It was a celestial feeling, seemingly without the restraint of gravity. As such I feel sure it could have been the perfect introduction to some religious experience, the dawning of grace, the merging with the divine. Do we all undergo this emotion, I wonder, as a rite of passage in our becoming, an intermediary stage in our psychological and emotional development? A preparation for the next love, the one with all the constraints – the one that knows you will have to return home in time for tea, if there isn't too much homework, ask for permission to go out again for a while without giving away too much... . The first one angelic, the next pedestrian...

In retrospect, none of my childhood infatuations measured up to my childhood holiday love, René-Jacques, the most beautiful, brightest and the most probable: there was a very good chance our relationship could have materialised in adulthood, except he died in a Vespa accident at the age of eighteen and left me drifting on unkind seas. I still remember the feel of our kisses, his warm insistent lips, the soft blond hair near his temples, his mischievous eyes and audacious spirit. All I have left of him is a small photograph where he is, aged fourteen, smiling cheekily at me. He now occupies the best frame on a shelf and I call him my love. It was all downhill after that.

*

I have a birthday coming soon, an ambiguous blessing at best. It is not the advancing proximity of death, which doesn't worry me at all, but what happens before, that distresses me: some would still call it 'life', but illness and the diminishing of my faculties are ghouls in my mindscape, and I would be quite happy to kill the body if I couldn't destroy the disease; rob it of its victory. Meanwhile, I would like to celebrate in multiple company this time, because, thankfully acquiring new quality friends, I feel less isolated and can at least celebrate that fact. Usually, my daughter makes a point of spending the day with me and surrenders with grace to a walk and lunch outside at Kenwood house if the weather allows. I relish her bright and spirited presence: she can be fun and serious, spares no details of her stories as she notices everything. She certainly can do 'conversation'. This is when she is the most herself with me, and I rejoice in her maturing certainties at the same time as I learn not to impinge. She feels safe since she knows I approve: her secure and joyful relationship with Adam, her professional conduct, her friendships. I find her clarity and sensitivity impeccable, which is why I find it difficult to face her judgement if I should take initiatives that she finds uncalled for, like talking directly to people to whom she feel she has priority of access: she then ruthlessly defends her territory. So I have been forbidden – begged, she would say – ever to intervene with her father, as if he was no concern of mine... . True to say she makes it a duty to see him, albeit rarely, while I have for many years now banned him from my house. He is her domain now, her responsibility, her business, and I have been told in no uncertain terms ("this is nothing to do with you, it's my life, please don't be hurt by what I say but let me say it, I'm so angry with you and so upset at being cross with you: I need to be separate, you have no right...") This is what happens when you have been so close; there was little demarcation during her childhood and we frequently merged, so that she cried when, after ten years of celibacy (she was ten then) I announced I had found 'a boyfriend', Paul: 'I don't want you to have a boyfriend! I don't want you to have a boyfriend!' she screamed through her tears. But eventually pacified by my assurances that although, as a mum I had everything I could wish for, as a woman I needed a man, she bought sweets to give him at their first meeting. Growing fond of him, she learnt that there were safe and reliable men, so she has one of her own now. But she will stand firm on her newly defined territory and needs me to pull back, as my own mother never could.

Where she is less her adult self is often on the telephone: protected by distance, she can easily afford the frequent contact that her affection dictates, and occasionally and unconsciously, I know, betrays the deference, submissiveness even, of the little child: her voice will rise one octave, her tone become childishly endearing: 'You are my mummy and I am your little girl,' it seems to say, and we are in one embrace, contented as cats. What is it she used to say? 'Mummy, I love you from the bottom of my heart, to the top!'

I tease her: 'You have your little girl voice again.' She laughs. We are both grateful.

Chapter Nine

Sunday morning and I have just bought the usual newspapers. So much to read, so much to know. I am hungry for it, yet can't say I like what I know. Even what is entertaining or elevating doesn't seem to compensate for the despair that fills me on confronting the poverty, hopelessness and cruelty of this world. Still I have to be aware, it is my world, it belongs to me, but I feel depleted rather than in any way fulfilled by its endless turmoil.

I am therefore lucky to be able to live in this glamorous little burrow, a small two-bedroom basement flat endowed on the garden side with a wall and ceiling of glass that reveal heavenly greenery, all mine, guarded by tall neighbourly trees: an undisguised blessing, a haven.

May has been so cold and blustery the squirrels seem to stay away, only reappearing between showers. Even the lilac, for once gloriously laden with bunches, has been beaten into submission by the heavy downpour and hangs helplessly, defeated: its blooms will soon grow black and rot.

It is a perfect day to read, though, and I will peruse the personal ads as an hors d'oeuvre. I note that the 'Christian Poet', weekly devising unwanted interests in his required lady-love, now forbids her 'fun', having previously deprived her of grandchildren, jeans, pubs, dancing and sport...

A little further on, though, I am given notice to go into action:

> – PROFESSOR, young 60, Francophile, likes politics, dining, dancing, arts, travel, seeks attractive, caring, intelligent F. Under 60, non-smoker, preferably over 5'5, for LTR. London.

Very suitable, I thought, – and begged myself to be intelligent this time and not miss a possible opportunity by replying two weeks late. While I re-read his details I find myself nodding: yes, young sixty will do; I am Francophile myself, like politics, dining, and it would be lovely to dance again; the arts: certainly, all of them; travel: yes please; attractive I am, caring, intelligent ok; under sixty I pass; non-smoker yes; over 5'5 too bad; shapely: yes, I have more shapes than I care to mention, and LTR would be my life-saving potion. Calling this evening, sounding positive, will be the right kind of response.

I surrendered to my own persuasive arguments. His name was Robert and he came from the States; semi-retired, engaged in research and writing, he was recently widowed and lived in Highgate; loved the arts, travelling and playing tennis. He was looking for a woman with her own interests and a caring nature.

I didn't mention my age in my response, knowing that the very fact that I was French would guarantee me a reply. 'As for my height,' I ended, 'I am under 5'5 but you'll have to try and be tolerant!'

What should I wear? What do I look nicest in, skirt or trousers? If my cupboards tell me to please myself, my heart sighs and says: why not wear something ordinary, there is nothing to celebrate, you cannot seduce a complete stranger and seduction could be the last thing on your mind. Yes, and not just ordinary, but chaste: while I often wear open tops, I decide to cover up entirely.

Robert telephoned the next day. We chatted pleasantly enough which inevitably led to some hope, and, when, twenty-four hours later he sat opposite me in a local café, I looked at him, an average-looking man, with conscious detachment. He barely rose as I approached, and at a glance we evaluated each other: he was on the plump side of average in build, with most of his hair in place, a soft light brown still, with grey at the sides. Nothing remarkable struck me in his features, when it could all have been redeemed by expression, a proper smile for instance, but one has to deal with restraint at times, timidity, or heaviness of spirit. Myself I smile easily, and try to make the person feel at ease. He was wearing a very nice suede jacket ('I have just bought myself a Pierre Cardin jacket,' he'd said over the telephone) obviously for such occasions; it was too early to comment on it, but it spoke of elegant informality. However, I sensed a cool examination of me, 'my type' – I am no 'blue stocking', and would not wish to look it. There are times when we instinctively know if there will be a future, and I was feeling remarkably indifferent. This was lunch and – unless he usually ate lightly, which his definite bulk denied – he chose it to be short by ordering a soup and a basket of bread. This was definite cautiousness, he may not have wanted to pay too much if I should take his generosity for granted. I did not want to embarrass him – I always pay my share – so to make things easier I ordered soup as well. He had a glass of wine, I abstained. We did the tour of interests already mentioned on the telephone the night before: France; his friends there; New Zealand where he lived for a while; was he in

Auckland, I enquired and he looked surprised I knew the name of the town. He was quite happy to talk although there was a heaviness in his voice, but he wasn't so interested in asking me questions about myself or my life. I volunteered a number of things that he didn't pick up upon, so to keep the balance, of power possibly, I told him my daughter had practically forbidden me to move ever again (we have moved five times together), and I would comply this time as this small flat of mine is paradise…

I must have been the wrong type for him too: he was a professor, his wife was a professor's wife, bookish as well no doubt, so possibly no make-up; I wear it discreetly but insist on it, this world has to be a prettier place. I was wearing a coat because the wind was cold this end of May but it was a spring coat, colourful, I call it my 'happy coat'; not sober evidently. Because I was relaxed he overcame his initial reserve and thawed a little, and the tone was safely friendly as we both knew this meeting was a dead end. Only when he reminded me: 'You know I'm a widower,' with some evident sadness did he touch me and I said that I was very sorry, it must have been very tough. He says yes, a brain tumour you know. Inoperable? Yes. It must have been very painful. I could see that although his wife died three years previously it still felt recent; the man was still grieving. I asked about his son, what he wanted to do after university; he didn't know. I said not to worry, he'll find his feet, young people do, we cannot interfere.

We finished our meal, his double espresso and my lemon tea. I took my purse out of my bag and paid my half. We were both grown up and could say goodbye easily. We shook hands on the pavement and I said, goodbye, Robert, nice to have met you – effortlessly.

I wished I had felt more for him as a human being, been able to say: keep trying, you are doing the right thing, do not retreat into your books: something didn't allow it. There was a slight dismissiveness in him – which may come easily to professors – when the student doesn't quite come up to scratch, or at least expectations.

It would have been unreasonable to feel despondent at this stage: the day was young, this enterprise had merely started and I was too old to afford myself an easy disappointment; there would be others. Maybe I could mitigate the inevitable waste of time by putting an ad in myself: receiving possibly numerous letters if my text is good, deliberating (perhaps with friends) the prospects and potentials of each. I wouldn't ask for photographs, they can lead to rushed conclusions, and I am not so superficial as to judge another merely on his looks (Emmanuel wouldn't have stood a chance, but this may be an argument to contradict mine). A photograph is static, a fraction of a second on someone's face while animated features, revealing character and emotions, disclose far more of a personality. Posture is also only of the moment, while self-expression in writing would tell more about the person. Besides, I will still be looking at the men's ads. Apart from my own search I am curious enough to follow the progress – or lack of it – of the Christian Poet, who has now come out of the closet and advertises himself as a 'Fundamentalist' pure and simple; and a newcomer to those pages, a 'Cultured Man, who has read the whole of The Encyclopedia Britannica' requests a 'studious woman'... . All that homework...

I finally select my text, for the Letters Only section (a very small section, when it exists at all):

SPIRITED WOMAN, French-born, attractive, young late fifties, educated and confident, interested in people, ideas, art, books and gardens.

I wish to meet a man of broad culture who is fit, solvent, caring, and capable of intimacy and humour. Box 1234.

Apologising to the gods for the lie about my age since I do not want men writing back to an old biddy, I pay my dues: at £115 for a single day, encounters are expensive, though not as emotionally expensive as hope can be.
And I waited.

*

– Letter No 1
Box 1234
Dear Spirited Woman,

Two things will already have struck you.
a) There is no photo. I do have one but it is out of date in that I had a short trimmed beard for about thirty years but am now completely clean shaven, apparently I now look a lot younger, and believe you me I was very gratified to discover that I did have a decent chin underneath it all.
I did try the Post Office photo booth but despite the fact that I can get on a stage and deliver a script with reasonable ability I cannot compose my face for a picture without looking like (if I smile) a simpleton with a lopsided face, or (if I don't), well put it this way even I wouldn't want to meet me on a dark night!
The reality is I am probably quite good-looking.
b) I live in Devon.
Don't let that put you off. I have no idea where you live but it would appear that the vast majority

of advertisers are domiciled in our capital, and I am quite well aware how (the mass media at least) considers that civilisation ceases at Swindon and that if you venture beyond Bristol you fall off the edge of the world. The reality is that I am only 2hrs 14 mins from Paddington and just a little longer to Westminster on the Waterloo line.

Since I am serious about finding the right permanent relationship I do not consider any form of travelling to be an obstacle.

I am 58, just over 5'10", slim with well built upper body (I am a rower and work out three times a week, not for fanatical reasons but hopefully to engender longevity and keep trim) and a head of full hair, some of which seems to have lost pigment, strange I am sure it was dark brown when last I looked.

I work for Devon County (not county hall, I am at the sharp end in an area office and definitely NOT the archetypal local government officer). I won't bore you here with what it means, save that I am a stand-alone officer and completely autonomous, which is useful in terms of taking time off but not so good when nothing happens at my desk during any holiday.

I have a waterside apartment which has what the estate agents are pleased to describe as having location-location-location but I am really a country boy and would like to sell soon.

I am very practical around the home (there is nothing I haven't done in terms of building or refurbishment), and in the kitchen I am simple but competent.

I don't have a vast appetite but I will go a long way for what I call real ingredients, I eat neither junk food nor take-aways (well all right the latter once in a while). And while I love eating out I do not have a passion for food per se, but will try anything and of course when abroad, always the indigenous menu.

However don't expect me to enthuse over such as bacon and egg ice-cream (A A Gill and Michael Winner – Fat Duck at Bray – choose your own camp).

Culture? Well I love the theatre in most forms and I occasionally get up to town for the likes of the Tate and I found the reconstructed Globe wonderfully exciting. I can tell you the actual (as opposed to the putative) famous last words of Oscar Wilde but I could not hold an intelligent discussion on *Waiting for Godot*.

I spent my childhood in books but I don't read nearly enough now although I do write a little, short stories mainly and always with a twist in the end.

I can't do serious poetry but I can do a reasonable line in satirical and humorous verse.

As far as retirement is concerned I see it as an opportunity in life not a wind down, but I have no intention of doing it alone. Life, whatever aspect of it, is less if not shared, and when I finally stop working I have a cunning plan.

And yes, like Mr Blackadder's it is a plan so cunning that you could stick a tail on it and call it a weasel!

I think that will do for now, so if you wish to know more my number is above and I have an ansaphone with my voice on it saying something probably silly.

In any event I wish you happiness.

James

I am very impressed: the man is bright, educated, can write, and is obviously professional in his endeavour; his letter is well composed, presenting concrete details with levity and intelligence, detailing the most important aspects of himself in a precise and personal way. He has worked on it, this is a serious exercise for him – and I should think this is a letter that he can send and does (why not be practical?) in its entirety to any women who appeal on the Friday, Saturday and Sunday pages of the better national newspapers.

I shall certainly contact him, but let's see what the week brings. I have been surprised by the promptness of his letter received only two days after my ad appeared. All the more surprised that, on reading his letter, I have realised that I have – unconsciously on purpose? – omitted to say that I live in London, so he is even more deserving of a reply. I am furious at my own stupidity, few people will bother to reply to a person who, unlike anyone else on those pages, doesn't have the wit to say where they live; I myself would ignore any such message, it smacks too much of the bottle thrown into the sea, and I no longer have the romanticism or the energy to pursue it. Of course, being in two minds doesn't help, a reluctance to engage in BIG FEELINGS once again, the anticipated exhaustion at a vital but dangerous journey, the concern that I now have less to give which would be unfair to anyone good and sincere. So I am now tripping over the obstacles I have myself put in my way, what an idiot...

There is another letter on that same day, from Essex:

Dear Box 1234, the spirited lady…

Sorry not a first growth Bordeaux or Burgundy but I come highly recommended with a dry mouth filling wit, a slightly spicy charismatic flavour as an aperitif, Kir or Royale, and carry a delicate intellectual bouquet being extremely versatile but need to be drunk quickly. Anyway I'm – Male, slim to medium build so lean and hungry like my hair, cut short, sixty-three, with two grown-up sons, professional background with some literary and philosophical pretensions (an old joke about being a legend within one's own lunch hour or underpants), fit and active, regular swimmer, enjoys reading and writing and making things. A bad linguist but trying to master French and Italian.

Tendency to spend spare time at the theatre, cinema, concerts therefore seeking a "good-looking chick" to hang on the arm and cuddle, with any kiss from the heart rather than the lips, as I have a very kind and caring nature (a steely torso with a thinning heart), so mollitia (see Latin "mollis") in character.

What was it about the myth of Psyche being inducted into heavenly bliss by Cupid, then sworn into silence about forbidden delights. Cupid sealed her lips by placing his finger over them, so what's it to be?…maybe I'm just of the hard-boiled, spaced out, street wise or of the hippy-dippy school of writing; enjoy the urban noir of mean streets and disconnected living in tacky suburbs, or again an old Whitmanesque dust-jacket in disguise, living in the countryside.

If anything grabs you in your elegant educated blonde brain (I might be just what the doctor ordered?), then give me a ring after 9pm in the week or take pot luck at the weekend to find a best friend, with luck even a platonic soulmate or lover!

John Witman

Chapter Ten

Two days later, letter number 3 is another kettle of fish altogether: a small brown envelope from Birmingham, whose very thin contents turn out to be one half of an already small writing pad page, indicating meanness of spirit. Handwritten, its tight letters however form scrawny and angry words:

Dear (?)

Can you send me more details: height, build, education, occupation, etc.?

I never get a reply when I write. They all expect phone or E-MAIL number or addresses. From my own experience, it is like a call-girl network. Not ONE mentions marriage. They all want long-term fornication or adultery (L.T.R.) or a 'relationship'. No wonder VD is rising among elderly women. You may not be like all the others, but that remains to be seen. They are so mass-minded.

Do NOT send this letter back with no full name and no address. I do not want a letter I can't reply to. If you don't want to write, then you should not advertise for postal replies.

Yours faithfully,

A. K. Morris

– Letter No 4:

(My interest at the sight of the next envelope, from the House of Commons, is short-lived: that name has been crossed and the word 'PRIVATE' written underneath. The gentleman, no gentleman in this instance, is into recycling as is confirmed by the bottom of the printer (Basildon Black and White 2), pages: 1 ; To Pay £0.10.) Mustn't waste, but taking it a bit far? Bad manners, I would say.)

Dear Advertiser,

Do I detect a French connection? In my experience small women mean big trouble! Especially if she is spirited! A good sense of humour helps deal with life, and I suppose your description applies to me.

Kindly tell me more.

I am 76, a youthful, healthy (touch wood!) version – widely travelled, I lived in Italy for 9 years and after four productive years in London where I enjoyed good life to the full, I set up my own business in Europe, mostly la belle France for 16 years.

Apart from trips to Canada, New Zealand, Middle East, Sri Lanka, several times in recent years, I have remained in England. In 1975 I returned from France to find family responsibilities, illness of Mum and a brother, both died 1980 and 1982 – a traumatic time for me. Since then one more brother and two sisters have died. So I remain alone, with several good old friends.

I am happy here in Sussex, the town has become very cosmopolitan and more interesting than before. I write and have poetry and articles published with much material in draft waiting to be made presentable for a publisher – a major task awaiting me! I seem constantly to be gathering new experiences and material for my writing.

I wish you good luck and health.

Yours truly,

Robert Castle

I have nobody but myself to blame for the paucity of the replies. Still, it is quite entertaining, I tell myself, although it also gets me down.

Another day, and three letters this time:

– Letter no 5.

Dear "Spirited Young Lady"

I'm not sure how one starts a letter such as this – this being my first attempt. Well, I suppose a few basic details are requested by yourself in order that you can build up a mental picture of the writer of this letter. I am 6'3 tall of slim athletic build, due to the fact that I exercise daily. My age is 67 and I have been told, recently, that I am "both handsome and pleasing to the eye" (hair and teeth are still in evidence).

My present situation is single. In the past I was married but now I am divorced. It is possible to say that I am fairly bright. Many years ago I attended London University, where I obtained two degrees and for most of my adult life I lectured in Economics.

Financially I am very sound, owning a large detached house in a pleasant part of South-East London. In the garage is a Mercedes, which I have owned since new.

I do not smoke and drink mainly wine. My interests are varied and include foreign travel, all matters financial, gardening, reading, dancing, theatre, Radio 4 and *The West Wing* – just to mention a few.

Please contact me should you like clarification of any of the points mentioned above.

Thank you for your time.

Best wishes,

Andrew

– Letter no 6:

Hello,

I like your description "young late 50's". I could make the same claim except it would be misleading. I am 61 (would you believe fifty eleven?) But my brain sometimes thinks I'm still 40 until my body sends a reminder.

You ask to meet a man of broad interests and I could be that man. Among my interests are walking, especially on hills and moors and I live close to Epping Forest and Wanstead Park both of which have a fascinating history; music, mainly classical but also big band swing and jazz; theatre – drama and musicals; most sports as a spectator; eating in and out; quiet nights in and noisy nights out but most of these are better done in company, after all a pleasure shared is a pleasure doubled. I am romantic, (passionate at the right times), but also practical. I know how to treat a lady and I try to find humour in most things.

I am fairly well educated to degree level, have all my own hair and most of my teeth.

I am single and have been for 8 years so no baggage. As you can see I live in London and if you are within reach of the capital I'd like to hear from you but I should warn you that my BT line has an answering machine that sometimes cuts off calls for no apparent reason. May I suggest email?

Over to you. Anything else you want to know please ask.

Regards

        Brian

– Letter no 7: (With two addresses, in Ireland and Holyhead.)

Dear Spirited Lady

I am an Anglo-Irish gent in my sixties, very fit; I have not been to a doctor since I was twelve years old.

I have a very wide range of interests been in Business and Farming all my life and am now

semi-retired and following my hobby of Antique
dealing and collecting

I am an old-fashioned romantic very capable
of intimacy with a good sense of humour, please
write to me at eighther address, I look forward
to hearing from you.

Yours sincerely,
Joe Heany

— Letter no 8 is a bit of a shock:

It starts with: 'MY DEAREST LOVELY SWEET
HART HOW ARE YOU THANK YOU FOR YOUR
REQUIREMENT FOR ACTIVE MAN WHO IS ABLE
TO INTEMACY. I AM 52 YEARS OLD AND ABLE
TO DO...

I can barely read it initially, holding it at arms' length
for fear of contamination, then enough to laugh at it,
defusing the tension that such intrusion provokes in me:
zero for spelling, the only correctly spelt word thereafter
is 'vagina'. And having fulfilled its purpose before being
sent, its envelope bears a second class stamp...

*

I think I shall go away for a while, France beckons, as an
old friend now installed in the region of Bordeaux where
I went to university is inviting me for a few days of sun,
good food and explorations of the countryside; I find the
prospect totally irresistible. I will also be in good company
which will lessen the need to pursue what feels at times
more like a duty than a quest, giving me a good excuse
to prevaricate yet again.

I cannot, however, ignore my first — and best —

correspondent: James. It would be insulting to act casually when he took the trouble to write such a good letter. I could, at any rate, ring him to thank him for it, and see what he sounds like. I have once again waited nearly two weeks before acknowledging his reply, and further delay would be bad manners. (Interesting to note that we often decide for ourselves – to suit ourselves – the boundaries of good and bad behaviour, the old codes have broadly disappeared in this age of laxity.) He might think I have been deluged with mail; or been too busy himself sending that letter of his to some of those charming and interesting, often younger women, who crowd the weekend newspapers personal pages. At least on the telephone he cannot tell my age, and I quite enjoy a disincarnate relationship at times.

When I ring him one evening, three days before going away, I get his answering machine where his voice, very male and self-assured, greets me in abstentia. A good message, and his own at least. I leave a message of thanks for his interesting and friendly letter, asking him to ring me back if he wishes, giving myself a sense of achievement and possibly of opportunity...

Three days pass and I am lost in conjectures: he may be away for the weekend; he is meeting other women; I am too late and he took umbrage; he is a cad, casual in his relationships, a man obviously to avoid...I shall please myself and go out any time I wish, instead of waiting by the telephone.

Returning home that evening after drinks with neighbours, I am shocked to hear, the moment I open my front door, a man talking in my living room: I am being burgled. I freeze, only to realise that this is a message being left, loud and clear for once, on my answering machine. I make myself a hot drink and ring back.

Well, my exchange with James was delightful, introduced by my story about him being a burglar – a very chatty burglar – and laughter is immediately an ingredient in our conversation. I feel happy and at ease. 'You have a way with words,' he comments at one of my jokes. 'Yes,' I reply, 'like George Bush.' He laughs. I love his laughter, loud and male. 'Do you know,' he exclaims, 'that he said that the French had no idea of the meaning of the word "entrepreneur"?!' And for ten minutes we exchange jokes about Dubya, an easy way to situate oneself politically, at least in foreign affairs. And France: he loves it, has friends there, adores the French temperament, the way they protest and demonstrate when they do not like something (I could myself give him a lot of pleasure in that area). His secret plan is in fact, after retiring – in two years I presume, he is a civil servant – to sell his waterside flat and buy a place in France.

'You make me envious,' I complain, 'I miss France so much!' And we exchange life stories: he was married to a teacher who became a headmistress, both of them having decided not to have children but concentrate on their careers. They later divorced, amicably I think. Then a long affair with a woman who had a little girl, and he enjoyed helping to raise her child. There was again a friendly separation.

I tell him about my various studies, jobs, my daughter, my present flat and garden. And then he asked: 'Hélène, how old are you exactly?' (True to say that I didn't describe myself with exactitude in my ad; to say: "young late fifties" is being creative with the truth, if true to my appearance according to my many witnesses.) Nevertheless, I am embarrassed. We are friends now: I shouldn't lie, I feel ridiculous. 'James,' I reply, 'I am a little older than you.' My God, another lie… . There is a short shocked silence.

'It isn't really a lie, James, I am going by the way I look, even my enemies would agree, even they laugh when I tell my age, please wait and see for yourself.' 'All right, if you're attractive.'

The conversation picks up again, to quickly recover and return to the easy exchanges that seem to flow so naturally between us, indifferent to the fact that we have never set eyes on each other. ('Right, Hélène, I think we should meet' – 'Would you come to London?' – 'Of course.') I like this man, focused, determined, practical, open. I love his voice, so male and warm. And I don't regret lying, he wouldn't have written to an old biddy of sixty-six. (Oh, my God, sixty-seven soon! I can't bear it.) As we say 'au revoir', he asks that I ring him on my return.

Chapter Eleven

I came back from a ten-day holiday on a Sunday, happy to be home, and decided that I wouldn't ring James that evening but the next day: this being mostly an exercise in self-control and for my benefit only since he didn't know the date of my return. Still, it didn't do me any harm, I assured myself.

I rang him on the Monday evening, but he was out and I had to leave a message. There was no call from him on the Tuesday, so I went to visit some friends nearby on the Wednesday evening. When I returned at around nine, his voice on my answering machine was assuring me that he would ring again. Relieved and delighted, I called back, but since he was out again, "I'm returning the call you were returning!" I said cheerfully.

Waiting was hard. I was in a hurry to be freed of any preconceptions I might have of him, mostly built upon the impression of his voice – the very physical presence it had – as well as on the intelligent liveliness and friendliness of our previous conversation. I wanted real, hard, unwarpable reality; even disappointment would at least free me from the pitfalls of dreams. There was no call on the Thursday, so I rang once more on that day, imprudently to my mind, nor on the Friday or the following weekend. Where was he? I felt abandoned, lonely. I wanted to meet him. I wanted his voice around me, that deep strong male voice, I wanted him in my life. The thought of him made me feel a woman, now vulnerable, and wanting… . Where was he? Meeting other women no doubt, there was no shortage of good and interesting – and younger – women.

My age worries me. My French friend worried me, scolding me at the sight of one of my open tops ("You're showing your breasts? You mustn't, it's all wrinkled, it looks awful." – which isn't true at all, though I changed tops to placate her – and showing discontent again when she later complained: "Why haven't you got lines above your top lip like me?" "Well," I replied almost apologetically, "I never smoked…" Although I felt under attack, I also understood her feelings, I hated all the sly, implacable signs of age which accumulated silently on my body too, but we age at different rates and it seemed I didn't deteriorate fast enough for her liking. Women my age often study each other's faces, comparing the cumulative defeats: there is rarely a glance free of anguish or possibly spite; the drama takes place in silence, the thoughts a language of badly hidden sorrow. No matter how much we value our and each other's experience, sophistication and knowledge if not wisdom, our preparedness for old age is more of a bracing up against the bad weather that awaits than a wise withdrawal from what invisibly animated us: our youth, our freshness, our cheerful energy, our ability to seduce. Few of us live it with equanimity.

For all these mournful feelings, letter No 9 – from Derby – was there to greet me on my return from France, to lighten me up and make me smile: "things" mightn't be so bad after all?

Dear box 1234,

Your recent ad in 'The Saturday Times' interested
me.

I am single, late 40s and would like to hear from
you.

I am also a university graduate and if you would
like more details you can contact me at the above
address.

I can also send you some photos. I used to model
as a male model for a U.K. Model agency.

I am pro-French and like French people thus
your ad appealed.

Enclosed s.a.e.

With very best wishes,

Tom Rayburn

Amusement is good for tension relief, and I am grateful
to all the good men of this world who enjoy an older
woman. However I shall use Tom's s.a.e. to thank him for
his nice letter and tell him I think he is a little too young
for me… . Answering any of the others is not an option
if I'm not interested in taking things further and I don't
think I am unique in this respect. Nevertheless, ignoring
some of my correspondents may not be wise; indeed some
of my friends have reacted with surprise at my intention
to ignore the lecturer in Economics, but I am not attracted
by people who display all their worldly goods, and his
mention of a Mercedes bought new doesn't impress me
because he intends to impress me with it; besides, the tone
of his letter, although not really objectionable, I find very
dull. It doesn't compare with the liveliness of James's letter,
in fact none of them compare with James's. I am aware
of being on slippery ground: becoming fixated on a man

I have only, after all, had one telephone conversation with. For all his charm, James is still an unknown quantity. And what about the man who likes walking in the hills, I liked the tone of his letter, but he didn't even say what his profession was: why? Of course I could ring him, a call would be easy – but it means engaging with yet another human being and I get at times a little tired of them. The seductive thing with James, apart from his intelligence and humour, is that he wants to go and live in France, a scenario that appeals to me – so let's not make that a trap? It would be easy to fall for a scenario...

The Saturday paper brings me some good news: the nice lawyer I had left a voice message for, albeit two weeks too late, is back: his same ad speaks of a 'man of sixty, six foot two, average build, cultured, caring, easy-going, warm, romantic. W.L.T.M. attractive, warm, attractive lady for friendship and L.T.R. Ldn.' He says 'attractive' twice, it's obviously important. He hadn't contacted me, my message obviously being number fifty or so and he gave up long before...I should be prompt this time, be one of the first by calling on the day. After putting it off until I have read most of two Sunday papers, I finally comply with my own command. It isn't easy, as I have to correct my message three times, ("I am in my early fift...", "I am in my late fifties/early sixties...") Deciding on my last try to leave my age a blank, – he may leave me the benefit of the doubt (a lawyer?) – I think I have a good chance of a call.

The lawyer, John, calls on the Sunday evening and conversation flows nicely. When I comment that this exercise we are engaged in is somewhat stirring, he replies, well, it is the modern way... . He works as he pleases, but obviously daily, specialising in property matters, and enjoys it. I tell him about my long career as a teacher, then as a counsellor and simultaneously an interior designer (therapy for houses). I now write. What about? The inevitable question. Well, it's about two sisters and is doing my head in…not a work of fiction. We agree to meet, and since he lives locally he suggests the foyer of a nearby hotel on the following Thursday.

The weekend is nearly at an end and James hasn't rung. Damn him. Am I being punished for lying about my age? Is he merely casual? I am a lot less anxious now, though, for my date with John: things are moving. But the telephone rings again shortly after ten and it is James making contact, bless him, and again his voice resonates. 'We have been playing hide-and-seek, haven't we?' I offer. His laughter is loud and easy. He is just back from the rowing club, the gym had made him thirsty. I was watching television, he hasn't interrupted anything important. He has something to suggest to me: he is going to spend the next weekend (another weekend without him!) with childhood friends in Northampton, taking the Friday off, and will be driving: he wants to see me on the way there, and so will be making a large detour although he wishes to avoid London, could I meet him halfway? Say around Luton or Dunstable? We could meet at one of the service stations off the motorway, 'It's just off the M1, it's easy for you, come on!'

So adventure is in the air. I want to meet him, but the prospect of a long drive doesn't please me: does he know of a specific place? No, he will ring again the next day so we can exchange ideas. I look at the map, it would be nearly a two-hour drive, and there is the question of where to meet. Odd idea.

When he rings the next day, I am diplomatic but adamant:

– James, I'm not very keen on your idea, you still don't know of a place to meet, it will be stressful, having driven in a rush there. You will be on your way somewhere else, with little time to spend together...

– Well, I was trying to be practical, combine the two...

– Well, what's practical isn't necessarily nice, is it? Look, I want to meet you but it's got to be right: why don't you come the following weekend and spend the day? Are you into art exhibitions? We get on well to talk, so we'll have a good time whatever else happens, and we could see an exhibition, walk along the river, have lunch, much more relaxed...

– I think you may be right...

– I thought I might be! Look, have a nice weekend with your friends and ring me when you get back, is that agreed?

– All right, then.

James has gone down on the scale of attractiveness: is he insensitive? Or is he just being a guy? I am pleased to know that we shall meet, but can now freely look forward to meeting John.

Who can I talk to about Anita Brookner and Hilary Mantel?

Chapter Twelve

What shall I wear? He is a lawyer, and not a young one, so I could be forgiven for thinking he may be in the traditional mould: living in Hampstead Garden Suburb doesn't describe him as a swinger, but we don't always choose – although if we live there, genteel, polite, well-bred, we do. I'm not prejudiced against genteel, well-bred or polite, on the contrary, only boring. Having grown up in a middle-class well-mannered family hasn't saved me from a world stultifying with its short horizons and narrow preconceptions... . And my later dealings with clever Oxbridge types familiarised me with arrogance and callousness.

What shall I wear? My day clothes on that day are pretty, feminine, but possibly a little too informal for a seven-thirty drinks date? The flimsy black trousers billow at the bottom like harem pants, smart though unusual on a woman my age. I will change: traditional black trousers and a cross-over top, black again but feminine and bust-enhancing, some nice jewellery; heels.

Are you nervous? ask my friends. No, I reply. This isn't an exam. I, a mere woman, am meeting a mere man. And I am learning to be without hope while remaining positive:

it should be a religion.... Besides, he sounded extremely nice over the telephone: divorced, three grown-up children and two grandchildren; a lot of books; enough work to make leisure welcome while needing to share it...

In the hotel foyer we promptly identify each other. He is wearing a light blue short-sleeved shirt to suit the good weather. He looks very unfit, being overweight with tired features making up a gentle face. With a slight smile he asks:

– Hélène?

– Yes, hello John, very nice to meet you. His handshake is limp.

– Nice to meet you too.

This foyer is a rather good place for encounters: without bright lights or music, it favours conversation. Other people are sitting here and there but not too close by. I must keep it in mind for future meetings.

Over his dry sherry and my tonic water our conversation flows: does he work from home? No, but he went home to change. You work in litigation, don't you? That's right, landlord and tenant law, property law, all that...

Two little children run past, who make me smile:

– What a sweetie!

His nice old beagle eyes are observing me, moved by my love of little children. In turn I am moved by the tender look on his face, he must be such a lovely granddad. He tells me about his work, that, however sympathetic he might feel towards his clients, he cannot take sides, and the law keeps him safe, dictating the outcome. He is curious of my past work as a counsellor, which I describe as the most intelligent and profound work. He wants to know how I approached cases: neutral sympathy, not empathy, enabling the person to take little by little a more active part in their own healing, through understanding themselves and their own lives.

A well-read man, he presently has several books on the go: Primo Levi, John Grisham, Julian Barnes... . He asks what my own writing is about – two sisters, their parallel lives, a family story in effect, of course greatly autobiographical. How and when do I write, did I always want to? Many men being in my experience mostly interested in themselves, I admire his openness and gentle curiosity, this man is a treasure – and as we chat, such is the feeling of trust that he inspires in me that I find myself slipping into confiding mode, so that, since he follows me on that new ground, we start talking as fellow travellers, colleagues sharing the same goals, and begin comparing notes on the people we meet. We are now on the same side looking for another, no longer possible partners ourselves. Having met 'a dozen ladies', he describes one twenty-five years his junior who was fine about his age. "I asked her: do you realise I could be your dad? But it didn't matter she said, her previous partner had also been in his sixties." I match him with my last correspondent who is in his late forties and had been a male model, and his face lights up with amusement. I have to confess that I am not myself in playful mode, finding our enterprise more serious and exhausting than fun – although, on a good day...

Of course we part as friends: "We have each other's numbers," he says as we shake hands, though we know we will not meet again; we have a job to do, must press on...

*

Sunday night and James must be back after his weekend away. I don't expect a call so soon; it would indicate an interest at this stage premature although it would be flattering; of course it indicates he has different priorities, but Monday night is much more probable. When nothing happens though, I lose my nerve slightly: what if his friends had dissuaded him to meet me, a woman who fibs about her age? whom he may find old in spite – or because of – her assurances? A reasonable photograph of me has lain on the coffee table for a few days, in part to reassure me: a smile on my face, my eyes still look sad and it cannot be disguised that my lower body is on the heavy side: it could warn him, though disappoint him if he likes slim legs for I cannot oblige. My friend Amy says that I'm prettier in reality; my feeling is that if he has changed his mind this could revive his interest: I shall send it, what do I risk? Is it, at my age, still a meat market?

On Wednesday evening my telephone finally rings:

– Hélène?

–Yes?

– James.

– Hello, James, how are you?

– Fine. Right: I'll be arriving at Paddington at 12: 17 on Saturday. (Is he in a hurry? How am I? Fine, thank you.)

– All right, I'll be there, and now you'll be able to recognise me!

– Well, I…

–You've received my photo, haven't you?

– Well…

–You haven't opened the envelope?!

We burst out laughing:

– Oh, no! I can't! I want the surprise…

I chuckle:

– I don't believe it, you should wear a blindfold as well!

– Oh, yes, you'll recognise me then, I'll be the man with a bandage over his eyes!

– James…how many times have you met someone this way?

– No…not often…in fact I don't believe I've ever done it… (Can't he remember such a thing?)

– Really? (I smell a lie, surely I'm not the only one?) All right, just let me say, I'm five foot two with short blond hair and blue eyes and I'll be looking anxious…

– Okay, and if I can't see you I'll open the envelope!

– Don't worry, I'll be there: I'll be the woman looking for the man.

– It's an adventure, isn't it?

When we say goodbye I observe that our conversation has been disappointingly short: is he in a hurry to go and meet his friends at the rowing club? – all single men like him, all divorced, living on stories and beer? Does he drink? Does he have a drink problem? People who drink always lie. I might observe how much he drinks over lunch although he might be on his best behaviour. However, he would only invest in 'best behaviour' if he likes me and wants to make an impression and then I wouldn't know…except that vanity could lead him to think he can make an impression without curbing his ways: "I am quite good-looking," he had stated in his letter. I remembered a man whose ad I had answered long ago: he had described himself as good-looking when by all reasonable measures he wasn't, but he was so bright and charming that I forgot about it completely over dinner, albeit marvelling at the self-assurance that mere conceit can lead to.

I am still under the spell of James's voice and laughter: we have laughed a lot in the course of our few conversations and a merry mood has cast us in the role of allies. The low manly tone of his voice, authoritative in its clarity and fluency, is incredibly seductive in an already physical way: music to my ears. What is my voice like to him? It is undeniably feminine, not croaky yet and so lies about its age. My laughter is a spontaneous burst of mirth often cheeky and unconstrained by propriety, but how affecting it may be is of a subjective nature, not for me to decide. Our voices together have created a friendly mix of observations and teasing: was there not an undercurrent of seduction? A mischievous precursor of things to come? Oh, I wouldn't presume, anything can happen, but indulging in conjectures can at least prepare me for the mystery of what is to come...

I have had, nagging my brain like the buzzing of a mosquito, the words of James's initial letter about Samuel Beckett: "... I couldn't hold an intelligent discussion on *Waiting for Godot*. Certainly I can see that Oscar Wilde has far more appeal for him and that if Wilde had spoken about the absurdity of life in his plays he might like him less, and cannot connect with the existential anguish of 'Godot'.Is he a superficial, one-dimensional man? Or were his words just banter? If I scratch the surface, am I sure to find the true man?

Why no children? Although it is an advantage at this moment in time that he doesn't have the distraction of a family – more time for me, for his French project – I wonder at the reasons why he and his wife decided not to have any and concentrate on their careers? The deeper reasons – for don't we all, the majority of us at least, want to create from our very being a new life? We seem to want to without even thinking about it: biological compulsion, social conformity, sentiment, all play a part. And while we are free to choose and no one should be forced into parenthood, my hunch is that there is a story behind the childlessness, a childhood story, an unhappiness there: maybe he didn't like being a child. And could I tell him about Hilary Mantel and Anita Brookner? He may not even have heard of them... .What is worrying James about me? Will he find me companionable? (We are, on the telephone, a good match). Attractive enough, not too derelict? He had been surprised to hear that I loved children and babies: does he only like women who don't?

(Oh, no, I remember, he had a liaison with a woman who had a young daughter and helped raise the child.)

I can't go on thinking like this.

Chapter Thirteen

The weather forecast is good for the day James finally comes to London, no need to put my umbrella in my bag. I can wear my loose feminine – and youthful, says Amy – clothes with a rather striking necklace I have made myself. I also take a guide in case we wish to go and see an exhibition, in case we run out of words.

I haven't slept well lately, unusual for me, only reassuring in that it means James may be worth worrying about; there's always a cost, I am reminded, not always the measure of value. I have been thinking about his liveliness, his sense of fun, all delightful. He said in his letter he was quite attractive: I hope he is right, although pleasant-looking – sympathique – would do fine. A bright and good-looking man his age can take his pick of good women, so why is he still on the market? Why did he choose to reply to my ad? It must've been a jolly good ad.

Suddenly awed by all that is at stake, I catch my breath before leaving the flat for a silent, still, prayer: Gods of the Universe, listen to me, I want to be happy, I want to be lucky, I am ready! Please no more misery and heartbreak. Please, joy and fulfilment. I could love a good man with all my heart...

*

Paddington station greets me, uncrowded on that sunny Saturday morning: with its large vaulted ceilings filtering summer light and elegant arches, it looks rather attractive for a last chance saloon. I am early of course. "I have short blond hair and blue eyes and will be looking anxious," I had told James. I must try not to look too anxious.

Only a few people are waiting in front of platform three. When the train finally arrives, five minutes early, I scan the passengers for a fit-looking grey-haired man who may or may not have a twinkle in his eyes, and of course I soon see him, eyebrows raised, his whole face a question mark. I nod with a smile, although I am not at all pleased: James is far too fit and handsome, too suntanned, and his bright David Hockney-swimming-pool eyes seem to reflect more blue light than I can cope with. I know the type, the tennis players with their sweaters casually thrown over their shoulders, parading in front of coquettish and flirtatious women. I am disappointed. The day will of course be pleasant but it'll be exhausting having to brace myself again for an encounter of insufficient content. As we talk and try to find our bearings with each other, I decide that his over-bright eyes make him look a rake. I'll bet he breaks hearts.

– What'll you have to drink? James asks in the outdoor area of a pub where we sit out our first act.

– Something exotic, like a tonic water with ice and lemon?

– No gin? He has a great smile.

– No, thank you.

He brings back an ale for himself and we are then at leisure to examine each other: he is wearing a light blue open shirt and light green casual trousers; a smart sweater in grey and blue checks is resting on his shoulders; good leather shoes. The umbrella he carried just in case is lying folded next to his beer, as is his newspaper. He is very tanned – or is he tanned over a ruddy complexion, his cheeks seem very dark? In my black harem pants (very slimming) and a loose bright green top with my home-made art deco-style necklace for impact, I feel reserved and cautious although I probably look at ease. He seems very relaxed, words coming to him fluently as well as laughter.

"It's an adventure, isn't it?" he had said during our last telephone conversation. Well, it is, and he seems to be enjoying it. I think I'll enjoy it too, but know that James is far too good-looking and fit for me, he can find far better, I'm almost an old biddy. He, on the other hand, has none of the dustiness of most men his age, none of the dullness: he sparkles.

We soon sparkle together. I have the feeling he likes me and he is wonderful company.

When I suggest we might like some lunch, in Covent Garden maybe, we call a taxi which delivers us there. The small French restaurant we stop at isn't full and we choose a table near the window, giving good light and a clear view on the animated streets.

It is easy to be friends with James. He teases slightly, but just as easily mocks himself and we adore the same old comedy series on television. We vote for the same middle-of-the-road party. His ex-wife and I share the same first name (I abandoned it in my early twenties). He describes himself, as I have always done myself, as a late developer, and we have the same dislike of technology. The synchronicity of it all quite takes us aback, possibly leading us to see our meeting as serendipitous, for we are getting closer in the three hours or so we spend over lunch. Neither of us is grilling the other but from time to time crucial or personal topics come to the surface, that we attend to seriously: belonging, my uncomfortable status as a semi-refugee in England; my late sister's religious vocation; and in particular James's grief at his brother's death a year previously: he admired his many gifts and loved him, the last of his family. I see that he feels orphaned as I do, and am moved by the trust he is showing me by showing his feelings: 'I am so, so sorry...'

When we finally come out into the sunshine, I lead him to the piazza, but we promptly find more peace inside the nearby church where musicians are tuning their instruments for a rehearsal. A short while later the sun beckons again and we find ourselves sitting on a bench in the garden outside among other couples, young people sitting on the grass and small children running about. We are full of words still and this time it seems we close in on each other, our glances are more aware of the other's and the liking expressed. The melting of my defences gives him access to freer looks and pauses when we merely smile quietly at each other. It all stirs a place in me where loves lives, asleep but waiting.

As we finally find ourselves in Paddington again and are about to part, I tell him how much I have enjoyed the day.
   − Yes, so did I, we must do it again...
   − Well, I might come to you next time...
   − Yes, and I will show you Devon...
   − That would be lovely...
He kisses my cheek and his lips slide to the side of my mouth. I must keep my eyes down or he will see how much I like him...

*

My thoughts are full of him, full of surprise and wonder and also of dreadful sick-making hope. His face, his blue eyes, dance clearly in front of me, his irrepressible laughter. I had imagined early on, because of the directness of his glances, that he may look very cruel when angry; today, however, he had seemed joyful and content.

Lying on my couch afterwards and my eyes drawn towards the garden, I lose myself in the peaceful evening light, and the branches gently shaken by wind. I am still with him.

– I'll make you laugh! he had exclaimed, you'll never guess what I nearly wore to meet you! The rowing club has a new blazer, smart green and blue stripes with the most amazing lining of deep red for contrast: genius! He chuckled. But then I thought: come on, don't be silly! Just be yourself!

I joined him in laughter.

– I would've been very impressed, but in a different way…

He had brought with him a two-page article that he wanted to show me about buying a house in a region of France until now relatively spared by the British invasion, the Limousin: did I know it? What did I think? I perused the article: quite a nice region, though not the most beautiful, terribly hot in the summer, he will have to explore… . Did he speak French? Well, just schoolboy French…he will have to learn, would he go to classes? He must start now…(do I sound too much like a teacher?)

– Which sign of the Zodiac are you? I asked.
– Cancer…
– Me too! What day is your birthday?
– Twenty-fifth of June (so did that make him fifty-eight

or fifty-nine? Please fifty-nine!) But I don't think there is much credibility in all that… . He looks a little haughty.

– Oh, there is some, I insisted, the generalities can be striking, there was a time when most of my friends were Cancerians. We're supposed to be family and home-oriented people, often over-sensitive…

– I would only describe myself as sensitive…

– I have been quite busy the last few months, I said, writing envelopes and distributing leaflets for the Lib Dems – some of them are near neighbours. I had always been on the left previously, but, you know, what with Iraq and all that's been going on, I felt I would be much more comfortable with them. Where do you place yourself politically?

There was a silence. Both his arms were on the table and he had become thoughtful.

– Yes, I also vote Liberal Democrat…

Why the hesitation? Was he lying? Or was he stunned at yet another coincidence? I am on the alert.

– What's the difference between 'gourmet' and 'gourmand'? he asked as we finished our meal.

– Well, a gourmet is a connoisseur, to use a good English word, and a gourmand is someone who merely loves his food, and may indulge, but one can be both!

– Do you still have your parents? I enquired: exploring family ties is a sure way to see how he has been affected by his childhood, as I want to try and understand his childlessness.

– No, my mother died some years ago, in a home. Visiting her there was AWFUL, and I thought – he became passionate, staring at the table and shaking his head – "Never! I will never end up like that if I can at all avoid it! And nobody would come anyway! I'd get a gun and do it myself, if I could foresee that outcome! Anything is better than that!"

As this is exactly the way I have often spoken to friends about that eventuality, I don't want to aggravate his mood by sharing it with him but am again struck by yet another similarity.

– What about your father? When did he die?

– Oh, I don't know, a long time ago...

– How old were you?

– I don't know... (What does he mean, he doesn't know? Anyone would know.)

– Were you close?

– No, he wasn't very nice. When he died, we felt it was no great loss...

He looked serious, but neither of us wanted to get into such depths at this early stage.

– Were you close to your mother?

– Fairly...she was a good woman you know, quite religious...

– Anglican?

– Yes, but I only learnt that much later, because I'd never been told – he chuckled – that we were High Church, you know, almost Catholic, and I helped at the altar, with the incense and all that...I don't go for those things now, not at all, he added dismissively.

– I was myself brought up a Catholic, of course, and left it all a long time ago too, but my sister became a nun...

– Really? he looked appalled. That's a bit extreme, isn't it?

I laughed:

– Oh, we don't do things by half in the family...I shrugged. We weren't in touch, and she died two years ago...

The way we paint the large brushstrokes of our past, informing each other of a heavy heritage which it is too

99

early to divulge in detail... . There is no such thing as 'no baggage'.

 – But your brother...?

 – He was so creative, so talented, he was the talented one in the family, I have no talent – yes, I can write, he conceded – but he could make anything, he even made musical instruments, the beauty of them! You can't imagine that he could manage to make them, with this piece and that piece, and it worked!

 – You must miss him very much...

 – You know, I forget at times, I go to work, to the Rowing Club, and then suddenly I am overcome with grief...

Straining not to weep, his eyes had gone red.

 – So there's no one left now...

 – No.

I felt so lucky that at least I had a daughter. And yet she was creating the beginning of a family now, away from me, as is in order... . A man would be a new family for me, and me for him.

 – How many letters did you get in answer to your ad? he asked, curious.

 – Nine.

 – Only? he was astonished.

 – Well yes! Of course! Because, like an idiot, being in two minds about it, having to do it because I didn't want to be alone any longer, but not necessarily feeling up to it – you know, it's exhausting – I wasn't thorough and so forgot to put: London! I myself wouldn't reply to an ad from someone who didn't put where they lived! It could be Outer Mongolia!

 – I have a completely different view! he exclaimed, emphatic. I would go anywhere to meet the right person! If it's important you go anywhere!

I was awed by his youthful idealism, he hadn't been broken, I felt grateful to be with him at that moment.

– Ideally, yes, but most of us are less romantic or more tired, which makes us less imaginative, more inclined to be practical...

And then, the most awesome instances of synchronicity between us: is someone or something pulling the strings? I was telling him about wanting to change my name, which was still my married name even though I had been long divorced. The name was useful, being fairly common which saved me spelling it to people, and easy to bear as I had remained until recently on good terms with my ex-husband. However, a new incident had brought to light the fact that he was still ready to exploit me financially. Feeling angry, I resolved that I no longer wanted to be associated with him.

– And to tell you another 'secret', James, the first name I use isn't the one my parents gave me, which was J. I hated it because I didn't want to be that person, I didn't want to be theirs, so I changed it when I was twenty-two...

He was staring at me, stunned:

– J. was the name of my first wife...

– ...so I have been thinking that I would like to change them both legally, which will be complicated because the French love paperwork, but I thought...you see, before my daughter I had a still-born baby, whom I called Thomas, and so I could use his name, and it would then be all about my own history...

He rocked back on his chair and his eyes were open in amazement:

– That was also my wife's maiden name...

We looked at each other, speechless, at a loss to know how to interpret this.

– Do you know what the probability of a second coincidence like this are? Millions to one... . One coincidence is nothing. But two...

– My God, James, this is spooky, isn't it?

It seemed to be pushing serendipity a little far, was it witchcraft? What did it mean? There had been so many similarities between us: as if he had been my unknown twin and we had led similar lives until our late meeting on that day...

– I disagree with you: to bear a name associated with such a tragedy would be harmful to you, it's not healthy.

– But it's no longer that, you know, I enjoyed being pregnant with him, I loved him, that's what it means now...

– I see...

There were happy diversions: in the church garden, sitting in the sun, I told him about my gorgeous daughter, my pretty garden, asked about his friends in France... . Time was passing fast, as our lunch had lasted over three hours and the poor waitress had kept coming in vain to ask us if we wanted anything else... . We didn't: our contentment had frozen both time and place.

Chapter Fourteen

The following day, a Sunday, was a day of grace. I was full of him, full of us, the profound harmony of the previous day was all-pervasive. Life indeed had taken a new turn and I couldn't wait for him to call, I wanted his voice, to know when we could meet again: next weekend? I could free myself easily. I imagined my utter bliss at being met by him at the station, a whole day with him of driving into the Devon countryside, looking at the sea, stopping for walks, talking, talking, and maybe taking risks, like holding hands.... It was all so heady, I felt twenty years old again.

Perhaps he would ring on Monday evening? or Tuesday? I had so much time to think of him. I remembered the expressions of pleasure on his face as he looked at me, which bordered on examination if I looked away, I could sense them and return to eyes that were in turn friendly, amused, pleased, moved at times. Touching came easily to him, reassuring for me since it proved, not only that he wanted contact but above all that he was capable of it, a rare experience in my life when the most significant men had proved incapable of demonstrations of gentle affection: my ex-husband; my daughter's father; Emmanuel.... There had been a moment – in the taxi – when our arms had rested against each other, and we had – I had – been conscious that that contact was good and sweet, and we had remained that way for a while, touching consciously, in an intercourse of sleeves. The warmth of it…a test of compatibility?

And, in the street, crossing the road or on the pavement, his arm lightly around my shoulders, my waist… . I had welcomed it, since he had felt like touching me. I had been more than usually discreet myself as I didn't recall looking – I am so moved by men's arms – for hair on his wrists, his shirt-sleeves had remained fastened and only the top button of his shirt was open. It was his eyes that I had connected with, and his laughter, the dancing looks in his eyes.

– I like your sweater, I said.

– Really?

– Yes, all these tones of grey and blue, very nice…

– It's casual…

– But smart. If I like it, I added mischievously, you can be sure it's good!

He didn't ring on Tuesday: how busy can a single man be in the evenings?

– Hasn't he called yet? asked my friend Alan who rang for news. You can tell him I'm very cross! I would've rung you as soon as I'd got home!

Wednesday night was a silent night, but my Australian friend Amy, after a long analysis of all the possible explanations, had another thought:

– He's English, isn't he? and we burst out laughing since we knew what she meant, I may well have come across (again) another example of British – they call it reserve – difficulty in dealing with emotions: facing up to them, accepting them, allowing themselves to express them…

– I am SUCH a late developer! James had exclaimed with particular intensity at one point, I struggled to remember the context without any success. What stage of development was he at? I would guess it was women who had pointed this out to him. It won't be as simple as I wished...

I was in turmoil. If I trusted in God I would feel like praying. A more helpful solution might be to consult the Runes. I had, on the rare times I have referred to them, been astonished and moved to tears by the accuracy of a reading.

I shook the bag, opened it slightly and blindly took one of the Runes out, the one that felt as if it was sticking to my fingers. I then placed it vertically in front of me.

Gebo X PARTNERSHIP. A GIFT.

Drawing this Rune is an indication that union, uniting or partnership in some form is at hand. But you are put on notice not to collapse yourself into that union. For true partnership can only be achieved by separate and whole beings who retain their separateness even in unity and uniting. Remember to let the winds of Heaven dance between you.

This counsel applies at all levels: in love relationships, in business affairs, in partnering of every kind. It is particularly appropriate when entering into partnership with what some call your Higher Self, while others speak of the interplay between the conscious and the unconscious in each of us. But most of all it is the case when seeking union with the Divine: God always enters into equal partnerships.

Gebo, the Rune of Partnership, has no Reverse for it signifies the gift of freedom from which flow all other gifts.

I had entered the world of the numinous – but didn't my conversations with James belong to that world already? I felt grateful, tried to calm my hunger. You don't hurry the Gods, even if happiness beckoned. I felt I should write to him; telephoning can be too intrusive and I had no wish to embarrass him. So on the Thursday morning, before going out with a friend, I wrote and posted the following letter:

Dear James,

I have decided to write to you because I am puzzled. Less intrusive than the telephone, this leaves you free to think your response – it may also save me from clumsiness.

It seemed to me that we had a great day together last Saturday and that we liked each other, so to be without news of you since then I find very strange, and upsetting.

Maybe I have misread all the signs. The way I felt, a certain 'protocol' of feelings meant that you would ring fairly promptly. Maybe you felt we didn't have enough in common? (I'm teasing you here! But it may be what has left you speechless...)

Whatever the reasons for your silence, I think I deserve better. You said you wanted to meet again? Why? Act upon it.

I certainly would love to see you. I am serious and clear in what I feel.

Happiness, if it is possible, requires courage. I still have some of that left.

Love,
   Hélène

When I expressed my anxieties to my friend, she scolded me gently:

– But it's only four days! (Nearly five actually.) You're too impatient, you mustn't rush him!

This made me regret sending the letter: I could be too impulsive, I hoped I hadn't done my cause too much harm.

Six days after my meeting with James, I felt very angry: there was no excuse. If he could ignore an encounter such as ours, he was worthless to me. I was very hurt, I couldn't bear to be dismissed so easily. What was in his mind? I also feared I might have misread him, but what was there to misread? And he was lost to me – and I was re-playing an old record, the same old record...

I was getting VERY angry, and restlessly ruminated:

He can only be forgiven if he has died: a heart attack on the train, no next of kin – the end. Or else he is in hospital, incapable of communicating, thinking of me but unable to speak. No one visits him. (The whole Rowing Club visits him!!)

He has an affair which he is finding hard to end: he is reflecting on his choices, prevaricates: he will ring me tomorrow, the next day.

He is working on a book on women and needed a new chapter: now that he has more fodder, he is busy writing. A short story evidently.

He is a rake, I was right: he merely wanted a fun day in London with a possible conquest.

He is married, needed some time off.

He has lost my telephone number but at least now he has my address.

He found me too old-looking, having been spoilt by the ladies at the gym: the sexy goodbye kiss was charity work.

He has been frightened off by so many coincidences.

He is meeting other women, so it's one at a time, he has to be practical.

He goes to French classes every evening till late. (What about a course in relationships?)

I was very calm the next day, the advantage of having burned myself out emotionally, this was welcome relief.

Hard though it might be to realise that I had misjudged our meeting, something else was definitely not right. I had to think back to some of the more revealing remarks he had made, both about what he would rather not speak about – his father – and what he needed to express – his grief at his brother's death: James was a very unhappy man. Finding himself alone in the world a year away from retiring gave the choices he had to make for the next phase of his life a crucial and awesome edge: "No one would come!" he had cried out when describing a dreaded end in an old people's home, since he had no children. And the obvious source of this, his father, since he had so hurt him as a child as to make him swear he himself wouldn't have any children. And what about the deeper fear that he might have inherited some of his father's traits? Also, the frustration with which he had exclaimed:

– I am SUCH a late developer!

He was cross with himself, took at least some of the blame for his failed relationships and was obviously afraid of repeating those experiences at a time when it was also urgent to form a new bond: "I would go anywhere to meet the right person!" But he also prevaricated, the feeling of urgency being so strong at times as to be overwhelming, so that it was a lot easier to go and socialise at the Rowing Club and drink with his friends. And wait, and delay, treating opportunities lightly.

It was during our meal together that he had pulled out of his pocket the still-sealed envelope containing my photograph: he'd wanted the surprise of seeing me for the first time at the station. There was also more entertainment value this way, giving the experience a tinge of excitement. He opened it in front of me:

– Very nice. Nice photo. Do you want it back?

– Not particularly.

– Was this your blue period? he commented as I realised that I had been wearing a top in harmony with the painting above me.

Recalling this exchange prompted me to wonder whether he had actually opened the letter I had sent him. I had better not care too much, this was getting painful.

In my dreams he would have rung me soon after getting back to Devon; he would have asked me if I was free to come the following weekend, which would have been wonderful; after which I could have invited him to the small party I was giving next weekend to celebrate my birthday for the first time in at least a dozen years, I had been feeling better about my life…

Would it help if I stopped dreaming? What if I stopped breathing altogether?

Regardless of the fact that his silence was inconsistent with our meeting – it wasn't as if we had disliked each other – I had to accept, however reluctantly, that it might be normal for him; and that, if this was indeed the case, I was in trouble.

"It is not," my mother used to say, "as I had imagined,"

and resented the whole world for it, and hated her life. I mustn't fall into that mode, I mustn't.

His abnormal silence – for he wouldn't behave in such a way in his professional life – left open the other scenario: he had been taken ill: if it seemed an unbelievable possibility, it was because he was the most unlikely candidate for early death. The loss of his brother had enormously affected him and would have brought into a harsh light the fact that, whenever it happened, he would be next, inexorably. At present, for all of his fifty-nine years, this tall and good-looking man appeared full of life and good health.

However, it was now essential for my sanity that I should become able to move on. So I thought I might ring him next week to say I was concerned to find out if he was alive and well and if so, to please tell me he didn't want to see me again and why. Unless of course his answering machine was on, as I still hesitated to ring his mobile.

Meanwhile, roll on another birthday…

*

As is usual with me, I'm afraid, I couldn't wait until the following week and rang his home number on the Saturday morning at nine forty-five and again in the evening, when I actually left a message:

'James, it's Hélène here, ringing you from London to say hello. I don't know if you remember, but we spent the day together two weeks ago…I have been very surprised at your silence and hope you are well. I also thought it would be nice to carry on our conversations and keep in touch. I'm sorry you're not in, so I'll ring again some time. Bye.'

On second thoughts, though, I won't, for James, in my emerging consciousness, is a cad. There had been, among the wondrous coincidences between us and the attraction

– which had started with his voice – smaller but indicative moments to which I should have paid more attention. Because they hadn't lasted and therefore weren't integrated in the bigger panorama, they could initially easily be discarded. Nevertheless, my disappointment and annoyance led me now to a less favourable and even less sympathetic assessment: I had certainly noticed that James never returned calls promptly, and had felt irritated by a possible lack of courtesy, unless he wasn't so 'on task' as he professed to be: socialising at the Rowing Club played a possible large part in that weakness, as I had never noticed that drinking in company made people any more thoughtful.

When I came back from France and he suggested a meeting on his way to Northampton, his casual choice of a motorway café as a venue didn't demonstrate sensitivity or even a sense of propriety: a teenager would have been more likely to make that suggestion and my friend Alan had been shocked : "For a first meeting? How unromantic!" My daughter herself had expressed horror: "I won't have you murdered by the side of a motorway!" I myself had thought it clumsy but funny: James was also 'a bloke'. I had of course badly wanted to meet him, which had clouded my judgement. The manner in which he tried to make me accept that chosen spot had been somewhat cavalier in tone: when I expressed surprise at his choice and reluctance at driving for a couple of hours towards an anonymous place, he had exclaimed impatiently:

– Well, I'm doing most of the driving. Come on! You drive, don't you?

During our meal together, he'd looked severely at my serving of mussels high up on the plate and exclaimed sternly:

– You're going to eat all that?

I replied tartly that I would leave out the shells. When

I asked about his place of work and whether he had other people working around him, he had replied contemptuously:

– To hear everything about their private lives? I am not in the least interested in their private lives!

I could see that he meant it. There was a coldness there, and so my first impression of James at the station had perhaps been right.

This assessment actually made it easier for me to accept his loss, or rather the defeat of my hopes, since I wouldn't have put up with such flippant behaviour within a relationship. A long time ago I would have clung (I did cling) to the most shallow and cruel man, my daughter's father, and the heartbreak that followed was unbearable. The lessons, however, had proved powerful to the point of being transforming, and I never again experienced the feeling of being at the mercy – partly due to my own acceptance – of bad treatment. Except, of course, from Emmanuel who exploited me so sweetly.

All this left me rather despondent and tired, though, on the eve of my sixty-seventh birthday. I needed a hug. I wanted a big soft creature around me, something like a huge teddy bear or a large cat: only I would be the one to sit on its lap with my head against its tummy for comfort, breathing in his familiar and soothing scent. It could watch television as late as it wanted as long as it stroked me from time to time, then I would be content. Right now, it would be enough.

Chapter Fifteen

Having stopped looking at the personal ads for a while, with the last few weeks full to the brim with thoughts of James, it came to me that it might be time to start again. By the look of it, many 'candidates' hadn't gone away: the Christian poet still displayed his fundamentalist edicts, having added: 'You must live alone and want marriage' to his usual list of forbidden sins like fun, grandchildren, drinking, dancing, and the wearing of trousers. The self-declared Angry man had attempted to tone down his text, but not his heart, by requiring a partner 'at ease with anger'. An 'Assertive male' of seventy-one sought a 'lady up to forty-five who would like the fun and laughter of a compliant relationship'. An optimist in his eighties – but why not? – wished to meet a lady in her seventies, since the functions of the heart do not stop until the heart itself stopped, the desire to love was anchored deep. We were all crying out for it, I should therefore myself re-join the more conventional flock and state my needs as well as scour those pages in search of someone who at the very least spoke the right words...

My first ad, omitting the mention of London as my place of residence, had turned out to be as effectual as a message in a bottle at the mercy of the waves. I had to do better now and not waste any more time. July was nearly over, lots of people would be away in August – with family? with friends? unless those who stayed were, like me, lonely and without much purpose in summer: August can be like a whole month of Sundays...

Like a votive note between two holy stones and among so many, I would place my ad in a Sunday paper this time, not that it should make much difference, but what about placing it in two papers rather than one? I would think about this further. Could I start today? Now? And this time it would be a voice box, not a 'letters only' enterprise, which could be more successful in case letter-writing intimidated people nowadays.

DINNER PARTNER FOR LIFE wanted by spirited, cultured French lady, late fifties, who thrives on good conversation and humour. You are interesting, attractive, caring. London.

I regretted the brevity of the text but I was limited to twenty-five words, so I couldn't mention books, art, gardens, world cinema, but these would go in my voice box message. And since I had rushed to do it all, fairly unprepared, before going to the library, I forgot to say I was attractive. I also, in one of my early attempts fortunately erased, described myself as having 'short blue hair'... . Leaving out an important attribute each time was beginning to look like a psychological experiment, but the part of me that was tired and discouraged merely shrugged its shoulders. Although I remembered that I had seven days to change or cancel it all: I was dealing with thoughtful technology here. Besides, requiring an attractive partner might well discourage the more modest applicants. I needed to be more thoughtful myself, for it wasn't as if age and beauty had ever really mattered to me: my daughter's father was bald and thirteen years my senior, Emmanuel was fat...James had briefly been a good surprise but looks mattered for the first half-hour at the most, when everything else then took over: personality, presence, an ability to engage, and so a pauper became a prince, as with love you are indeed handed a crown.

I was still trying to be positive without being driven by hope, but all this – and the summer, and the happy couples who seemed to live in it, all this had put such yearnings in my head...

Navigating day after day on the various currents hopefully leading to love on this uncertain map, the outcome of the journey could at times appear hazy, like a mirage, its shapes in a state of flux: to arrive on its shores would be the culmination of one's hungry pilgrimage towards bliss, the yearning of the soul for recognition of another's, but also the confirmation of one's goodness and worth, of one's existence almost, and the reaching out for touch...

I breathed deeper, I often sighed. My heart felt larger in my chest. My lips swelled also, I caressed their softness with dreamy fingers. I tossed and turned in bed, at times reaching to the left side where the other would be, imagining the skin, the warmth. My body was hungry still and my arms full of emptiness...

I lingered in bed long past the normal time – seven-thirty, eight perhaps, to be reminded of what the nuns used to tell us at convent school, to get up as soon as awake lest the Devil did his work (the little devil that reminds you that you are fully alive).

My thoughts at times wandered towards coarser future realities, the pick-and-mix – the gravel in the sand – of daily living, unavoidable but still odd, other: his socks; toothpaste; vest and pants; body odour; hairbrush and comb; favourite pullover, feel of outdoor jacket fabric; walk seen from behind; sniffling (handkerchiefs or tissues?); heart or blood pressure tablets...

I also felt like cleaning the flat again and the urge to buy more flowers, the red and pink blooms of love, tidy the garden, fill my fridge with fabulous food, change the sheets for softer ones still...I suddenly became more susceptible to birdsong, wanted to go for walks in the park, buy a new dress...I might be sixty-seven but the heart was up to its tricks again...

Chapter Sixteen

"Life is sweet…" Joy had said, dreamily, and indeed it was – for her. I had been stunned, three or four years ago now, as I looked at her in her beautiful Primrose Hill house, a still young and active woman in her fifties, her short curly hair surrounding a face that had kept some of the gentleness of her childhood years. She and her husband – a handsome and friendly man quite a few years her junior, had been, after an impecunious start, very successful in their respective businesses and enjoyed a train of life that most people would envy: his flying lessons, their travels and second home in Italy… . They were good people, socially conscious and active, who still loved each other.

I had been shocked to realise that for some, life was indeed sweet, peaceful, rewarding: apart from my relationship with my lovely daughter and for the briefest of times it had never been so for me, on the contrary, while Joy and her husband had met very young and had known from the start that their path was a joint one. I often imagined that this could have been the case for me with René-Jacques, my childhood sweetheart, if he hadn't died at the age of eighteen in that Vespa accident, but the ineluctable fact that previous childhood traumas needed to be worked through would, at some point, have caught up with me and marred that possible harmony.

Joy and her husband weren't the only happy couple to fascinate me. I now had more time to study other, close people, and I could see that those happy couples were now showing me friendship or at least friendliness as they would never have done in the past. It was as if, feeling a pariah with happiness, I was treated as such by those who, unlike me, "knew how to deal" with love: could it be that my imperfect and clumsy loving over so many years, my agonising over my life and headlong efforts to right so many wrongs, were in the end producing some results and, being different, I could at least appear less forbidding to the contented others so that they were now able to include me in their fraternity? Could it be that I had become one of them and I was finally right for love?

At least my own ad would appear on the following Sunday. Action sustained me; it was also good to have my work to occupy many hours of my days.

When my ad came out, I read it again to try and ascertain what I feared was a certain degree of coldness: didn't I swap 'dinner partner for life', which had charm and warmth, for 'conversation' which could be deemed too intellectual? I was no intellectual, I merely used my brain, and frequently not enough of it. My worst mistake in my eyes was the use of the word 'requires' which could be regarded as arrogant, instead of 'seeks' which is humbler. Plus the fact that the limit of twenty-five words caused me to drop the word 'humour', which mattered a great deal. Did I really have to include 'fit and solvent'? On reflection, I thought I did.

Perusing the competition brought one delight:

– CREATIVE, OHAC (own house and car), warm-hearted female, 70s, non-deviant, slim, healthy, inherent Queen's English. You: unwhiskered similar. Suggest live separately and meet for highlights.

I instantly felt love for that woman: what spirits! She suddenly reminded me of a recent Channel 4 five minutes documentary which had depicted a woman of ninety whose personality and femininity shone through the screen. Although she was sitting down she seemed tall because of her good posture, and was filmed grooming herself. Combing her long grey hair in front of her mirror and deploring the fact that with age "everything had gone South", she stressed the necessity of looking nice, and her husband liked it. Plucking a long hair off her chin (I could see another one which she missed) she talked of her sexuality and pleasuring herself at night (it also helped her to sleep) which she would recommend to anyone. Then applying a bright red lipstick to her lips, which suited her vivacity, she wrapped an equally bright orange scarf around her shoulders while speaking of her attraction for her husband ("I've always liked him as a man..."). She was preparing herself for a date with him.

I was full of admiration: anyone, to my eyes, who broke the mould, ignored the usual expectations, put expressions of life in place of the morose if not despairing landscape we are supposed to fade into, was an icon of hope. Her refusal to conform and hide was no less than revolutionary. I wished I knew her, my ninety-year-old friend. We, the ageing people, disappear in so many ways before we die but she was saying: 'No', a beacon.

*

As it happened, I already had three messages in my voice box on that Monday lunchtime.

The first one was indifferent and ended: 'I'm not sure I am what you're looking for…' He would be, if he had truly read my text and listened to my voice message. The second one, who sounded Asian, was a kind man who was self – employed as an electronics engineer and did charity work in his spare time because he was lonely. I deleted them both.

The third one was an increasing surprise: "I liked everything you said," he started, sounding warm and pleasantly surprised; he could fit the required description, he assured me; he worked in the Arts and the theatre and wrote novels, had been on radio and television both as a commentator and interviewee. He went on to describe himself as sensitive and educated (Oxbridge). He liked all sorts of serious music and visited art exhibitions. "It does sound as though we'd have a lot in common," he concluded. When he left his telephone number, I realised he didn't live very far away.

I was suitably impressed, also a little intimidated: if he was such a star, I would be in his shadow and I'd had enough of living in the shade. However, the possibility of good conversation and a stimulating new world was not to be dismissed.

And then his name: Harold. This reminded me of someone. Could he possibly be…? I couldn't recall his surname, but hadn't I met someone answering this description…some twenty years ago? My daughter was then about five years old and I was lonely. I had put an ad in this same Sunday newspaper, asking for a good man who would be my lover and my friend, and this very man, I thought, replied. I couldn't remember where we had met, but a second meeting was at my flat: I had, clumsily, invited two of my friends to give me their moral support — as well as their opinion. We had become ill-at-ease and self-conscious, ending up launching into an animated conversation...about cats. I can't remember if he took much part in it. He seemed a good enough man, but I didn't like him and, having decided not to follow it up, promptly sank, as was my tendency at the time, into despondency. I gave up all attempts of meeting anyone for another five years. I moved houses, moved on...

Some years later I recalled hearing his name on the radio in an item on a novel about the sea, but I was no longer sure of his surname by then.

This time however, the description of his work, added to the area he lived in, gave me the near conviction that it was indeed him, and I was able to recall his surname. This was a stunning and hilarious coincidence, the very same man replying to an ad of mine after twenty years. Moreover he had become a well-known and prolific author.

I started to dream, invented all sorts of conversations, all manner of questions. I'd want to ask: do you write about what you've learned, and do you learn from what you write? Does it form a theme you didn't know about and which illuminates you? Also: who brought you up? I mean apart from your parents, some teachers perhaps, but those books you read early with which you identified? which would have helped you during all these sad years at boarding school maybe? For me, and long before Simone de Beauvoir who started Feminism with *The Second Sex*, long before Betty Friedan and the other American sisters, there had been Jack London: *The Call of the Wild*, *White Fang*, lived by my bedside as a young adolescent. I adopted Jack for my father and he taught me courage, endurance, the later ability to challenge and fight...

After a few days I rang his number:

– Hello, Harold, it's Hélène here. You left a message on my voicemail a few days ago…

– Ah! he replied warmly, I was hoping you'd ring!

– That's a very nice welcome…

– I loved your ad, and was happy to see that we liked the same things…

We engaged immediately, amicably: my English was very good, and so was my accent – well, I'd been here long enough – except that some people… – oh, yes, I know, it can sound abominable! You live in Hampstead, don't you? – yes, in much too large a house, so I'll be moving to a smaller place in Belsize Park in October, but the stress of moving and selling!

I chose not to tell him I knew who he was at this stage, easily done as he was keen to learn about me: what did I do with my time? I told him I wrote poetry and had published a dozen poems in reputable poetry magazines; about a book, two-thirds written but in abeyance, I'd go back to it later. I was a little older than I said, but didn't want people to reply to an old biddy, I spluttered, since, I added childishly, I wasn't an old biddy! We both laughed. I told him of working in the library, where I was writing a second book on love, loving, 'how to deal with it'… . Working there was so much more conducive to concentration than my flat, with my garden, my birds and my cat… . He had a cat as well.

We agreed to meet on the Saturday evening. I suggested neutral ground when he offered that I came for drinks at his flat: a nice pub in the neighbourhood instead. Then dinner? I asked laughingly, do you think we might have enough conversation for dinner as well? I could book in a small Greek restaurant I know. – All right, you book, for eight.

I was livid with myself. I couldn't believe I had spoken

so loosely, betraying myself stupidly at the first opportunity. What was he going to think? Couldn't I have waited at least till we met before admitting to the venial sin of lying about my age? (Not even that, being actually true to my appearance?) It put me at a disadvantage for I had broken a rule, however superficially, and I was sure to pay for it.

When I returned home after work the next evening, there was a message from Harold on my answering-machine cancelling dinner ("pressure of work, you know") but keeping to the seven o'clock date for drinks. I didn't believe his excuse, I knew he was backtracking, and he slid down somewhat on the scale of desirability. This had the effect of making me even angrier for having let myself down in such a pathetic manner: certain arts I definitely do not master! Why did I give myself away so blatantly? I disliked lying, certainly, and obviously couldn't wait to have everything in the clear by telling him the truth; this had been encouraged by my relief and pleasure at possibly finding a compatible mind at last, causing me to lose all sense of self-protection: was I still a willing prey after all the lessons I'd learnt?

The next day – the day of our meeting – Harold rang again: he was terribly sorry, so many deadlines, he wouldn't be able to make it for drinks either and, by the way, would I mind very much sending him a photograph?

I burst out laughing:

– God, I've worried you, haven't I?

– Well, you've played with your age…maybe it's better to postpone our meeting and I'll be a lot freer next week.

What could I do? Nothing but rage. I was offended, hurt, humiliated, let down. I was outraged: how dare he? Who does he think he is? Did *I* ask how old he was? Did

I ask him what he looked like? Does he think he is a godsend to women whatever his physical condition? After a certain age none of us are particularly fresh-looking, does he think it is only a problem for women? I put a reasonable and recent photograph of myself in an envelope, promptly drove to the address he had indicated and put it in his letter box. I drove fast, angrily. I wanted to run him over…or at the very least squash his monstrous ego.

The following day was a Sunday, my daughter's birthday as it happened, and she and her boyfriend were coming for a festive breakfast so I could give her her presents – they were meeting a crowd of friends for lunch. It was a joyous occasion but I was still seething inside, and Amy, who came for a drink later, agreed with me that his attitude was insulting, that Harold was saying in effect that if I didn't look good and young enough as being in my late fifties seemed to imply, regardless of my other attributes, I wasn't worth talking to.

– Drop him, she said, disgusted at Harold's insensitivity. You don't need that… . I had to reason with her:

– Amy, you're a happy woman, so you are spoilt, and unrealistic. Men are imperfect creatures – women sometimes too! I have nothing of the happiness you've got, and you've had it for thirty-five years… . I have to be patient with this man, because he sounds interesting, he has qualities and I have to explore that, besides I have no choice. But I'm not going to make it easy for him…

I'd write him a letter:

Dear Harold,

I have been thinking, since we last spoke on the telephone, and the words 'goose' and 'gander' came to mind, so I feel it would be only fair now if you could send me a recent photograph at the above address.

I hadn't thought of making this a part of this exercise, since it has always seemed to me that if two people liked each other enough on paper and on the telephone, they would be happy to meet simply as human beings – and let that meeting decide if there should be a further one, or not. Photographs often lie, and after all, it is personality more than looks which decides the issue.

Since you think otherwise, you won't mind my new request.

I shall be quite busy this week but may be able to find some free time at the weekend.

A bientot, maybe,

Hélène

I felt vengeful but admired my unusual restraint: I would have been entitled to require a photograph of him without a hat, for I remembered clearly that the photograph he had sent me twenty years ago represented him with a cap while our subsequent meeting revealed him to be seriously bald, so he was obviously self-conscious about it (how old had he been then?). I hoped my request would cause him the same agonies of self-doubt that any ageing women would go through when fearing to be judged inadequate, I wished him a sleepless night or two, I hoped he would be alarmed at the thought of losing, at least, the opportunity of meeting me.

*

There were two other messages on my voicemail to distract me:

– John was an architect who worked in Central London but lived in Surrey, and would love to take up my offer and looked forward to my call. He loved his work but wasn't very good at conversation...

– Peter was an Oxfordshire astronomer who talked at an incredible speed, stressing the key words and seemingly without stopping, which had the effect of making me feel instantly breathless. He was single, sixty-five years old, financially secure and "FIT AS A FLEA"; he was also five foot ten and dressed with style; oddly, he remarked, EVERYTHING I said applied to him; he was keen on ALL cultural pursuits, ALL the arts, and in music ANYTHING from the baroque to modern adagios; he had A LOT of energy, was a keen gardener and relaxed by walking; he liked talking ("I talk A LOT!" he threatened, as I gasped for breath).

They were both deleted, and I decided to repeat my ad for the following Sunday.

*

I wondered if my letter had offended Harold – it was intended as a stinging and ironic reply – perhaps he would decide not to reply. That would be fine by me. But if I didn't meet him I couldn't tell him about our meeting of twenty years ago? That would be such a pity, such an amusing coincidence should be shared...proving at least his attraction to the sort of ads I wrote. (Could I show him some of my writing? Would he be interested? Or condescending? But surely, he would like some of my poems?) And what had his life been like in the last twenty years?

When I returned from the cinema the following day – Sunday – there was a message from Harold thanking me for the photograph and suggesting we met at the beginning of this week: Monday or Tuesday? Could I ring him? – So...I had passed the beauty test, I thought sarcastically. How wonderful, I should be grateful, shouldn't I, and relieved, and feel blessed... . However, I chose not to ring him as he would receive my note on the Monday and should, I hoped, feel a little humiliated: didn't I say I was very busy the whole week but might – just might – find some time at the weekend? Would he rush to the nearest photo booth, cursing it in advance for an unflattering job? And finally, would he understand how insulting his attitude had been?

Tuesday's mail came with the required photograph. It was a rather poor colour photocopy of a photograph of him on a background of Italian or French landscape: he was standing, dressed casually, cap in hand I noted, and my memory of him was confirmed, but baldness had never been for me an impediment to liking a man. A handwritten note on the side of the picture apologised for the bad quality of the print. This isn't what bothered me. What disturbed and appalled me even, is that Harold, judging from this picture, looked to be in his eighties, so I was even more furious with him now: what did a man who looked that old think he was doing wanting to meet a woman in her fifties (as advertised) for a possible life partner? How on earth did he feel entitled to take umbrage when I subtracted a few years from my official age when he looked as if he could be my father anyway? The arrogance of the man! I didn't care if he was the Einstein of the literary world, if his intellect was massive and his career brilliant, his ego seemed even more monumental! I wondered what Mrs Einstein had felt and was instantly full of compassion for her... . And Harold wasn't just old, he was very ugly indeed, in a sad and dried up way, in a forbidding way...

I felt so infuriated I no longer wanted to meet him, his behaviour had made him too unpleasant: what would be the purpose? To be friends? I didn't feel remotely friendly towards him, and if I didn't he obviously wouldn't want to know me. I could only imagine telling him off from the start for being so high-handed with me, punishing me for a misdemeanour by cancelling our dates and taking refuge in a request for a photograph. Who did he think he was? Had he ever taken a good look at himself? Found himself attractive to women at his age? I remembered very well having already thought him unappealing twenty years ago, the reason why I didn't see him again – but of course never said so, if indeed I said anything at all. One just didn't. The telephone went silent, the postman didn't call. Silence, that was all. That's what handsome James had done to me, even more cruelly after asking to meet me again, which left the door open to all sorts of wild imaginings.... Men were so other, so foreign : yet it remained true that I wanted one in my life, simply because I was a woman. The conundrum...

However, it crossed my mind that I was being hard and a little unfair to Harold: didn't I believe in the meeting of minds and personalities? Hadn't I told him so, proud to take the upper ground? But of course – and this struck me with the force of a gust of wind – he had taken my letter at face value, saw no irony, no sarcasm...men with such egos cannot imagine that a woman might not want to know them, it would have been therefore much more comfortable for him to believe that now having to send me a photograph – no matter how bad the quality – was fair enough, wasn't it? I couldn't see him for a few days? Of course, women were often busy, shopping generally...

What men were good at was the internet: using my own pc as a word processor mostly, I wasn't confident enough to play with it to source information, and so asked Amy's husband if he could find out how old Harold was.

My own attempt at looking in one of his books at the library had left me without answer, only with the feeling that I should read one sometime, they were highly regarded.

Now I knew: Harold was seventy-four. "My God, that's old!" I thought at the same time as I was pleasantly surprised he wasn't eighty. Perhaps Harold wouldn't look so bad after all? It was such a poor print, it wouldn't do anyone justice, although the blurring could be very flattering to some...I would meet him then. We were reaching the end of the week, today was Friday: was he anxious now that I hadn't called him after receiving his photograph? I had said I might have some free time over the weekend, but had deliberately given preference to Amy tomorrow and my daughter on Sunday, I didn't want to crowd my days, that's how I lived nowadays, pianissimo.... My ad would be coming out again on Sunday and I would be quite pleased if he saw it before I met him, it would let him know that there were other avenues for me. I should therefore ring him on Monday.

Chapter Seventeen

When Monday came, a day of almost unremitting greyness, I wondered, looking at the sky, if it would be the start of another quiet or eventful week? I would call Harold of course at some point, but I should also access my voicemail to see if there were any replies to my new ad.

The gentle American voice talking to me belonged to Bob, retired, who was doing a PhD. He had a flat in London in which his son lived with his partner and new baby. He could meet me in London for lunch at his club or any other place of my choice. He had lived in Britain for thirty-nine years, had an expensive education (Harvard), loved visiting art galleries. He was also learning French and could now just about cope with the subjunctive... . Apart from the fact that I was amused at finding another Devon man (I could visit him there and possibly bump into James!) he sounded an interesting man, although his voice, a little scratchy, gave him away as possibly elderly, or temporarily unwell.

Lunchtime loomed, I decided to ring Harold: had he resigned himself to the fact that I mightn't call? It pleased me to think I might have worried him, I owed him that. The conversation was short:

– Hello, Harold, it's Hélène here, how are you?

– Oh, hello, fine, fine… . He sounded surprised.

– I was wondering, would you like to meet sometime?

– Yes, yes, what about Wednesday? Just a minute, let me have a look at my diary… . Now, Tuesday would be better…

I suggested a café instead of a pub, it would be quieter.

– Now, what time? he asked. Seven o'clock?

– I would prefer six o'clock, if you don't mind. I sensed that he minded, he probably had set himself fixed hours of work and didn't like to default, but my Weightwatchers meeting was at seven and I didn't want to miss it again. Was he truly as rigid as he seemed on the photograph? On the other hand, you didn't write as many books as he had if you weren't disciplined.

Our encounter would of course be quite short, but I didn't really care now, having lost my initial interest for him since his fuss about my age and particularly the photo fiasco. I also needed to find my feet, a proper balance, a better view of things than my unruly mind had allowed me to grasp so far: there were some fears, indeed panic, in my rash judgments and passing of harsh sentences, and they were due to my concerns about age mostly: so Harold was seventy-four? He was only seven years older than me; my daughter's father was, at eighty now, having an affair with a woman of seventy-three… . But seventy was really old? Fairly. However, I was slowly getting there myself, I would be seventy in three years… . So there wouldn't be time? Time to live, enjoy, love, play, work, travel, there would probably be illness if not death, and it would all stop and I would be alone again…

*

When I rang Bob in the evening, his soft American voice

sounded warm and pleased to hear from me: he lived outside Plymouth – the proximity of a university and good medical care was essential – in a small village where cats and gardens had their importance. His PhD was more of a book than a thesis it seemed.

I was aware of thinking thoughts and judgements about voice, flow, length of flow, endless flow, getting a little bored – but why not let him be passionate about what he did rather than be impatient about when a more reciprocal exchange could take place? This was merely the first conversation.

He has a son and a daughter, both living with partners he liked, we agreed on the immense comfort this gave us as parents. He suggested we had lunch at one o'clock at his club on Thursday. I asked how I should recognise him. When I was bold enough to ask for his age, I sensed annoyance: 'I'm in my early seventies,' he said dismissively, 'five foot ten, grey-haired (or did he say bald?) with an Italian appearance, and I would be well-dressed because of lunching at the club…'

As I entered the date in my diary, I felt at first satisfied, then despondent: another old man who required a woman fifteen years his junior…I should cancel our date tomorrow morning, there was no point: he lived out in the sticks, he was elderly, and I wasn't sure we would achieve real conversation either. It would be unfair to let him think he had a date.

– Hello, is that Bob?

– Yes…

– It's Hélène here. Look, I have been thinking, I don't think I'll be meeting you on Thursday: there is too much of an age difference, and my interests are more literary and London-based, so I don't want to waste your time, I thought I'd tell you now…

– Oh, all right, then…
– I do wish you luck, Bob.
–Yes, thank you…
– Bye…
– Bye…

As I sat back on the sofa and automatically picked up a newspaper, I felt ashamed and guilty at my own double standards: men wanted a younger woman for exactly the same reasons I wanted a younger man: a younger face to look at and pair oneself with, reflecting a younger self; prolonging youth; postponing old age and its attendant consequences; being less afraid…besides, Bob mightn't be more than five years older than me. Had I looked at myself lately? (Yes, anxiously, more and more.) He seemed a really good man, genuine and in the world, passionate about his research… . My own interests weren't truly literary, I wasn't that well-read… . I suffered from a surfeit of preconceived ideas that just wouldn't stand up in court, I decided. And just this morning, I had noticed for the first time that the veins on my wrists were getting thicker, bluer…

I sat down feeling quite desolate and silly when the telephone rang and startled me. As I was feeling sleepy I decided to ignore it, but Bob's voice appeared, insistent, and I listened from the couch:

– Hello Hélène, it's a short time since you rang me… . It's a strange thing but if your literary rule is so important to you, it would be worth having lunch so you'll see for yourself that I'm rather well connected in that area. The editor of a literary magazine is a friend and my nephew is senior editor at a well-known publisher's. I am rather familiar with the field. If that's any help to you, so be it, I'll be delighted to have lunch with you. Bye-bye.

I felt full of remorse.

*

Meanwhile, I prepared myself for the meeting – the date! – with Harold at 'Black and Blue' (why didn't they call it: 'Bruises?'), one of the pleasant cafés on Haverstock Hill. Some people were already having dinner but the still early hour, six o'clock, allowed ample time for tea before my Weightwatchers meeting at seven. An old man with very white hair was already sitting at a table but he seemed so engrossed in his newspaper that I doubted if he was Harold who presumably would be looking out for me. For now, I was myself on the look-out.

I instantly recognised the man who, on noticing me, stopped with an awkward twist of his body – had he suffered a stroke? was he unwell? – The bald head of course, but particularly the very thick dark red lips that gave his face such a clumsy and unsightly look, and I remembered the man of twenty years ago. He was smiling broadly and we shook hands.

– Nice to meet you, Harold.

– It's nice to meet you, at last! he exclaimed, stressing the last two words, alluding to the several hurdles we had inflicted on each other. I didn't react, as doing so would seem as if we had already entered into a relationship – we had indeed – and I was withdrawing fast, in distaste, appalled at the idea of a possible pairing. But I felt grief for him also: he did look about eighty-four, this man who had objected to my being over sixty, he looked grey of skin, sad of features and unwell, how could any woman be drawn to him? Still, I was wrong about his health since he talked about playing tennis three times a week in the neighbourhood as well as attending a Pilates class. He had a good voice, deep and warm, and I tried to concentrate on the conversation: we both loved listening to the radio, Radio 4 of course, although he deplored the fact that it had dumbed down over the years, "and all these accents you heard nowadays"; he was no longer asked on programmes because of his own accent, he was certain of it. He had mentioned, when we had spoken on the telephone, having met Simone de Beauvoir in Paris and there had just been an item on her that very morning in the context of feminism. I said I'd thought of ringing him to let him know (men like him don't listen to *Woman's Hour*) but refrained because I didn't know him well enough. I nevertheless attempted to describe it, rather clumsily as it happened: Germaine Greer, I reported, found Simone de Beauvoir to be a much clearer philosopher than Sartre...

– Really? he said, that's ludicrous.

I had meant to say 'writer' – I know her work well – but, being the prey of yet another 'senior moment', couldn't think of the word and tried unsuccessfully to disentangle myself, no doubt failing the exam, and feeling crushed, like a ballet dancer (of course) tripping onto the stage at a main role audition. I was luckier with other areas: my preference for Camus over Sartre, the fact that you could have talked about football as much as philosophy with him, his all-roundedness. I disliked Sartre as a person, but admired his childhood memoir: "It's a dishonest book, you know," he commented, "he altered quite a lot of the facts..." We spoke of our children's happiness; moving to a smaller home; throwing some books away or not: I had; he just couldn't, did that disqualify me? But I wasn't in the running. When I finally mentioned my Weightwatchers meeting at seven, aware of stressing the mundane and not caring, he concurred about our need to stay fit and healthy, and after agreeing that it was nice to have met, I left him, saying:

– See you sometime, Harold... – hoping I hadn't sounded too flippant. He didn't ask to see me again either. Now indifferent, I had no need to berate him for behaving in a high-handed fashion: some people just have to live with their ineptitude. Telling him about our meeting of twenty years ago would have been pointless, tantamount to saying: I hadn't liked you then either... . It wasn't funny any more.

*

Having somehow 'buried' Harold and switching my attention to Bob, the telephone on my lap and a cup of redbush tea in my hand, I finally dialled his number:
  – Hi, Bob, it's Hélène here.
  – Oh, hello Hélène, how are you?
  – Bob, I'm contrite... ('Contrite'? I've never used that word before! Do I sound literary enough?) I get cold feet sometimes, so I'm sorry: I will meet you on Thursday if you wish...
  He interrupted:
  – ...and I was telling myself: "There you are, you've done it again, you blew it, you talk too much..." – I do talk too much: that's what I was trying to say, it's awkward at first, you're not sure what to say the first time...
  – Yes, and I was silly, so I will be very happy to meet you as agreed.
  – Good, so same time, same place, then.

*

When I arrived, on time, at the Landsdowne Club, I was quick to admire its traditional prettiness, the intricate plasterwork enhanced with gold, the graceful columns. I hadn't been to such a place for many years and relished the new experience and change of decor. Looking up the few steps that faced the entrance, I saw a few men seemingly waiting and was saved from confusion by a particular man looking at me who quickly raised an eyebrow. I smiled in acquiescence, it had to be Bob. We shook hands. I wondered later if he had been somewhat nervous at meeting me since he didn't seem to remember the floor of the dining room and we made a few trips up and down in the lift before he found it.

The dining room was large and light, with a high ceiling enhancing the art-deco features, particularly a superb fireplace of deep orange marble. We were sat at a good table by an efficient head-waitress who immediately brought us the menus. Talking about the choice of food was an easy way to break the little ice there was, and I could observe him as we spoke: he was dressed very formally, as suited the style of the place but not the fashion which had relaxed somewhat in recent years if not decades. I thought that, living in the country now, he didn't often need these clothes, and took them out of his wardrobe for special occasions: a dark grey suit accompanied by a beige waistcoat that was possibly too tight, he had a little paunch. He had described himself on the telephone as looking 'rather Italian', and I saw what he meant: on a background of serious suntan (he had just spent two months in the South of France on an intensive French language course), what hair he had left on the sides of his head, shaved to within a millimetre of his scalp, had been dyed a harsh black, probably the night before, as had his eyebrows: these had been hacked rather than trimmed, in an effort to restrain their length. The effect was rather contrived, but combined with the otherwise mobile and lively expressions of his ordinary features, it resulted in giving him the appearance of a cheeky mafioso, a sort of fully-grown Danny de Vito or an older Berlusconi before the hair transplant... . A fairly friendly look.

– Shall I test your French? I teased, looking at the menu: what is a 'crotin'?

–You find it on the streets, he smiled.

– That's right, I concurred, I rather fancy one, a little goat's turd...

– Yes, I think I'll have the same, that sounds very good.

We moved on down the menu and agreed again on the calves liver with bacon and creamy mashed potato and caramelised onion. House wine was served. I was making an exception, as I didn't think I'd be feeling sleepy today. I was very surprised to see our liver arrive without the first course, and he replied evasively when I told him so. 'You simply didn't order it, that's why...' I commented to myself. It was delicious nevertheless and the house wine excellent. I'd recommend to anyone suffering from the blues a good lunch with an agreeable stranger in an elegant place, for the conversation was flowing pleasantly along. He did talk too much, but he had a lot to say that was interesting about his years working for television in the States ("if you stay in this business, it kills you, the stress of it...") and he was familiar with show business too. I mentioned my close friend Alex who had written a musical based on a famous French book – I helped, over the last two years, liaising with the French side, and I wanted it badly to succeed as my friend had fallen victim to Parkinson's disease and he needed something happy in his life. As it happened, a friend of Bob's who also suffered from Parkinson's was on a wonderful medication that seemed to suppress all the symptoms without causing unpleasant side effects: could he ask his friend what the drug was and let me know? I asked. He would.

He mentioned at one point a play by Harold Pinter and he knew, he said, lightening up, a few stories about him...

– Come on, I goaded him, give me a few tidbits!

– Well, my son was at the same school as his. You know about 'Sports day' in English boarding schools, don't you? The races, the egg and spoon race and all that…?

– Yes, I know.

– Well, Harold's son was about to win the race, which was easy for him as he was very big and tall, except that he stopped just short of the finishing line to let one of the younger and smaller pupils win…

– That was so kind! I exclaimed.

– Yes, he was, except that Harold rushed to him in a fury and shook him and threw abuse at him for not winning…

Bob had a lot to say about the countries he had worked in, and his German, he told me, was much better than his French, but it was his later career as a management consultant that brought him to work in London, and to keep a base at the club. His PhD wasn't mentioned this time, but there were more stories about South America, Brazil particularly and the social divisions there, the terrible inequalities, and the casual attitude to the fate and lives of the street children… . There was a heart in that man. The fact that he did most of the talking – I prompted with a question, the odd comment – allowed me to eat, I was very hungry. When he had to catch up, it was my turn, briefly, and I could mention a little about my background: growing up in a dead-end town in the Pyrenees where my father worked as a lawyer, a tyrannical up-bringing, a later tendency to depression (touched upon lightly) and the influence of Jack London, "my adopted dad, who brought me up"…

– What about the literary connection? he wanted to know.

– That was more a part of me getting cold feet, I am not that literary, I laughed, I love and read all sorts of books, novels, biographies – a biography of Proust by Ronald

Hayman at the moment – that's all, and I write poetry, some of which, about a dozen poems, have been published in good poetry magazines...

– How about the theatre? Are you interested in seeing a play one of these days?

– Yes, certainly, I'd like that.

– I'm not sure what's on, I'll have a look.

– Oh, you know, there is a play, it's been very well reviewed, of the interview of Nixon by David Frost, it sounds fascinating...

– Yes, well, I'll look in the papers, he said a little grumpily as I realised my politics were showing once more and he might have taken offence.

When the menu reappeared for our consideration, we both chose the same dessert, what looked like a mini Tarte Tatin, and my allegiance to Weightwatchers melted in my saliva at the very thought of the pleasure to come... . Was it for the same pleasure that he chose to skip the starter? To have a dessert, for he wouldn't have both? For he most definitely didn't order the 'Crotin de Chevre' we had agreed on... . This man wanted things his way.

I also knew there was no question but that he would pay the bill: a man didn't invite a woman at his club in order to go halves. For my part, I usually paid my share when I went out with anyone, when I didn't actually pay the whole bill myself, but that was with Emmanuel...

When we left a little after three o'clock, I asked if he would like to join me at The Royal Academy to see the Summer Show, "and we can cuss all the horrible things there!" He declined, suddenly looking very tired and old:

– No, he said, I think I'll go home now, I'll take the tube to Waterloo...

He walked me to the entrance of the gallery, and as we said goodbye, he added:

– By the way, I am glad you didn't cancel...

Neither Bob nor I contacted each other again.

Chapter Eighteen

I was a little tired of all this, a little dejected. I had occasionally thought of throwing in the towel, this search appearing at times futile and possibly hopeless. I put my tea down on the table by me and took in the peaceful orangery I was sitting in, the warm colours, the small couch furnished with multi-coloured cushions covered with old Japanese fabric; the large paintings on the walls and the small Art Deco side tables; the enveloping cream-coloured armchair I was in by the window and the long cherry wood table I could write at: some files were piled up on one side, a golden lamp stood on the other, and if I put a thick cushion on the chair in front of it I was then able to work as well as properly own this space, the birds and the squirrels, all this belonged to me... . By the right foot of my chair, near the secateurs and my somewhat muddy garden shoes, was a bag of seeds I kept there for the birds, and raisins for my familiar blackbirds...everything was relationship.

I would like to tell him, THE MAN, whoever he may be, that I went to the cinema yesterday to see an Australian film, and since the afternoon was devoted to pleasure, bought one hundred grams of jelly beans, loose, from the sweet counter, to be savoured with the relish of guilt during the performance; they were in fact devoured by the end of too many trailers.... Then I nearly fell asleep a quarter of the way through but startled myself into alertness to rejoice as the film finally bloomed. I had an unusual glass of wine on my return, being normally sober in deed if not in thought, and lost myself in contemplation of the outlandish purple gladioli on the mantelpiece: could I tell him how I had changed my mind about gladioli? I had judged them pompous and arrogant in the past, so sure did they seem of their nobility. Supercilious, they looked down on you – a lower class of being – ever aspiring to sublime height and style, as if human fingers should remain low on the stem, never to soil the aristocratic silk...until one day my friend Marianne painted their portrait and I understood the other subtler features, the natural grace, the spiritual elegance, the individual striving of each single bloom to join in the slowly developing climax...so there they were, in my living-room, understood and appreciated. Five stems for ninety-nine pence at Morrison's.

I could tell him the cat had to have five teeth removed the other day and looked poorly and sorry for forty-eight hours, until he found his appetite again and finally enough lust for life to bring in a garden mouse that he played with all night, keeping me awake. I didn't mind, I thought it funny, I was happy for him if not for the mouse which I managed to catch in the morning, right from under his nose, and release in the middle of the garden, under the ivy...

Would he be interested to know that I was planning a trip to Edinburgh now the festival was over, by myself for once, which I am normally loath to do – to see an exhibition of sculpture by Ron Mueck? I was in awe of Mueck's work which I had seen previously in London two years before, the way that, not quite a plagiarist, he presented the human body on either a vast or minute scale but intimately, provoking a stunned contemplation of ourselves. I would go by train, with a good book, find myself a reasonable hotel, and take the two days as they came. It would be my first visit to the city in forty years, since my ex-husband Paul's first exhibition at the Traverse Gallery, which allowed us to spend a long weekend there. We were just married and so called it a honeymoon, although there was no sex, but that is another story. It was freezing and we had to keep putting money in the meter slot in our hotel room to stay warm. There was no slot for Paul.

Could I tell him I'd visited my GP recently because of having felt dizzy on a few occasions? I had known my doctor for well over twenty years and had stuck with him in spite of moving areas because we liked each other and I respected him in spite of his grumpy moods. I had been concerned that my dizziness was age-related or a symptom of something dire, but he reassured me, mentioning my inner ear. Would I dare say that, as he examined one ear, his other hand gently and deliberately cupped my other cheek, which I noted was unnecessary but tender, and so I welcomed it, almost closing my eyes?

I might tell him I had looked again at my book on Magritte's, to be entertained at first, but led to wonder if his work, as the other Surrealists', hadn't been the by-product of the First World War, a time when familiar reality had been so shattered, its centre of gravity exploded, as to be judged incoherent and represented as such. People who haven't lived through such disintegration never need step into the absurd, do they? What did he think? He. Him. Who didn't sit at my table or hold my hand, who didn't talk to me. Whose place was empty in my bed. Whose absence left me cold all over...

144

Imagining, if not anticipating, being in love again filled me, simultaneously, with a nervous anxiety similar to fear of flying, a balloon released to unknown winds…I knew that I could again lay myself open to exploitation and betrayal because I was (we are?) when I loved, childlike: love is childlike, child's play, all that appears is a given, and then…a large sticker across my heart warned: FRAGILE.

It was the same with friendship, allegiance: there had been the visit to my flat once – at my invitation – of Tina, the psychotherapist who had been my supervisor during my training as a counsellor. I had great regard for her subtle judgement and insight and she praised my work at the time, which made me feel valued. I had gone to her for help, three years previously, at a time when I had felt at my lowest and needed to pour my heart out to a witness who not only knew me but understood what I was going through. Her subsequent visit a year later had been my opportunity to show her how well and full of energy I now was, and the healing comfort I drew from living in a wonderful place full of light and views on beautiful trees. We had tea, chatted amicably, I was keen to show her that I was now better equipped for happiness or at least contentment, that I felt I had a future at last. When she got up to leave and I opened the front door for her, she stopped on the doorstep for a moment, looked at the steps that separated my flat from the pavement above and said:

– These will be difficult, soon. Still, you won't need to go out every day…

*

The next message I listened to on my voicemail belonged to Mick, six foot three, green eyes and fit, a retired graphic designer who for thirty years had his own consultancy and now worked from home, as he pleased. He was divorced with two girls of twenty-two and twenty-seven. He enjoyed the good things in life, eating, cooking, travelling, and now did a bit of painting and visited galleries. He also liked films. He used to play rugby but had now converted to golf. He took occasional holidays. What he wanted was someone to share all these things with: his voice, on my voicemail, had risen to capital letters, "to SHARE these experiences"; his loneliness reached me, echoing mine.

So I was sitting again at the terrace of "Bruises" that September Wednesday morning, when I saw Mick crossing the road at the pedestrian crossing exactly opposite me. He had exclaimed, when we spoke on the telephone and decided to meet:

– I know! I shall wear my striped t-shirt, very colourful, vertical stripes of blue, red and cream, you can't miss me in that!

If it sounded like a flag, I was pleased at the thought of an older man in a t-shirt, better than a three-piece suit any day, this wasn't a gentleman's club occasion; I welcomed the fact that he was six foot three, I like tall men, and I didn't mind 'follically challenged'; slim with green eyes and fit-looking would do fine.

We smiled as we shook hands, and I swallowed hard in astonishment: I had before me a younger version – he hadn't mentioned his age but I suspected we were contemporaries – of my daughter's father, David, who was thirteen years older than me, which made him eighty now. I no longer talked about him and would hate him more if I despised him less, for his shallowness and cruelty, his total lack of a moral code and complete indifference to the consequences of his actions. I had for many years forbidden him access to my home since, a long time before, having to save myself from him and my unhealthy passion.

Only my daughter sees him, seldom, reluctantly and dutifully.

David's eyes; his mouth nearly, the way it shaped almost into a beak on pronouncing certain sounds; his colouring and height; his bald head and side hair... . The nonchalant manner he had as he walked, crossing the street, which belonged to tall men at ease with their bodies; the way he sat, wrists resting on his knees, rocking slightly as he spoke. There was a man called Mick underneath all that...I had to find out about Mick, I had to be reassured.

Trying to be objective I thought he looked nice, unassuming, relaxed. I was wary of finding him pleasant, I sensed danger, in myself if not in him. I wondered: who was this man? I knew about his work, his daughters and their jobs and studies, his tastes in music ('very catholic'), his English friends who live in France near the region where I was brought up; that he paints a little ('oil, my flat reeks of oil and turps, I quite like it actually'); the disappointing fact that he doesn't read many books. ('Jeremy Clarkson recently, but it takes me all week to read the *Sunday Times!*'); when he told me he went food-shopping in France regularly – did he say every two weeks or every two months? – I nearly swooned and begged: 'Ooh! Can I come with you? He loved the ferry and making an overnight trip out of it; I imagined his kitchen cupboards full of luxurious French food – and rosé wine, he added, so wonderful and cheap!

– Have you had lots of replies, Hélène? he queried, alluding to my ad.

– It seems the love business goes very flat in August, I quipped, you were the only one this week. I explained about the ad being free to advertisers, who only pay to retrieve their messages.

And then, spontaneously, I dared take a shortcut, thinking

it would take me further, quicker (if he was clear-sighted, sincere, unafraid) :

– If you were to put an ad in a newspaper, how would you describe yourself?

He looked blank, his eyes, wide open, stared ahead. There was a long silence.

– I have no idea…

– Really?

– No, I couldn't say…

I was amused at first, then wondered if it was funny:

– WHO are you, then? Tell me who you are…I tried to joke: remember you only get twenty-five words for free!

There was another silence.

– I don't know, I really don't know…

I found that extraordinary: how was this possible, a man in his sixties? How could one properly BE without knowing oneself? Surely, he was intelligent, educated, had been married and had children, got divorced, and the latter usually taught you a lot more than you wished to know? Wasn't it like living blindfolded, at the mercy of others and events? I had felt moved on hearing David Blunkett speak with heart-breaking honesty about his disastrous love affair: "I misread the signs…" You don't need to be blind, although it evidently helps.

I couldn't quiz Mick any further at this stage, but my head was full of questions. This would be for another time if there was to be one. We had already sat talking for an hour over our respective teas and had got on very well. He hadn't asked me any personal questions although I made it clear I was retired, but he had volunteered that his daughters had remained with his wife after their divorce, "so they had a pretty good idea of what I had to put up with" (Was he saying that he had left his wife?)

He knew this area of North London well, living not

very far away, and had once lunched at the Tapas Bar along the road. September had slipped in gently and it was still warm enough to sit outside. An old woman having coffee at a nearby table had brought her Siamese cat with her and the animal was sitting contentedly on the next chair, creating a diversion: when she went to pay, holding the cat in her arms and walked past out table, I showed interest, smiling and as I raised my arms to stroke it, she obliged and we chatted briefly. I thought her probably lonely, using her cat to attract some attention to herself.

As I was getting hungry but didn't wish to leave Mick, I volunteered cheerfully:

– I don't know about you, but I get very mean when I'm hungry, would you like to share some tapas?

Mick smiled and made to get up:

– Well, of course – wait, I'll get this, and I'll get the other thing as well...

Did we want some wine? the young Spanish waitress wanted to know.

– Well, I don't normally drink at lunchtime, but it would be nice...

– Yes, he confirmed, we'll have wine.

– Rojo? I attempted.

– No, señora: tinto! El vino es tinto, y questa – she pointed to her top – Tshirt es roja!

– You're a good teacher, señorita!

Mick and I took turns choosing tapas from the menu. A large glass of Rioja came with them, adding to the festive mood.

– I love the Spanish language, I commented. A while ago, I thought of reviving my Spanish – I had done some in secondary school – and started attending a class at the local UTA, you know, the University of the Third Age...we had a terrific teacher, a Spanish woman full of enthusiasm, she was brilliant... It's silly but I couldn't bear to stay: all these old people, it reminded me of the home where I used to visit my mother – terrifying – and it was as if someone had pushed me in there, saying: there you are, it's your turn now, I felt like running away screaming...

He smiled:

– I suppose you could have gone to a College of Further Education...

– Yes but the nearest one is much further away and you can't park there at the time of the classes... . It was silly of me really, I should have been more broad-minded – and less afraid...

Rioja helping, was I revealing myself a little too much?

We moved on to politics via the opening and subsequent closing of new hospitals because of their financial problems:

– You know, they would run much better without any patients! Mick remarked with irony.

I burst out laughing:

– That's what I was thinking, but you know, they have already started, they try to throw you out almost as soon as you get in!

I had always situated myself on the left, I confided, but moved over to the Lib Dems recently. A neighbour had been elected a councillor and I had helped them with office work. That's where he found himself too nowadays, he concurred, a long journey from the Socialist Workers Party of his youth!

If I was right in thinking that political choice usually stems from a disposition of the heart, then I knew this man had a heart: journeying that far along the political landscape couldn't have taken place without heartache and self-questioning.

I was conscious of finding myself drawn to Mick who didn't seem indifferent to me, and felt vaguely excited by what I considered possibly the beginning of an event, so rare was it − and was terrified that the same chemistry was operating that had drawn me to David in the past, an irresistible force that had torn me and my life apart, after which I had spent ten years on repairing the damage, in therapy, celibacy and loneliness.

I had to call time, stressing that I should already have been hard at work in the library. I was glad to have a genuine occupation that I could hide behind so as not to appear too available, too ready to prolong the good humour − best that he was disappointed than that I appeared in a hurry to start a relationship, needy, and possibly sexually tempted... . True to say that neither of us had used any of the usual tools of seduction at this stage, and I couldn't presume that his friendliness was anything other than it appeared. However, the meeting couldn't be called casual for the very fact that we were openly two people looking for a mate and this put us on notice not to behave rashly: we were no longer young and couldn't use the flimsy excuse of thoughtlessness, we were supposed to show judgement and maturity; we were duty-bound, in our quest, to be conscientious, so that any development would be meaningful. I wouldn't say that my cheerful disposition during our encounter was devoid of a desire to charm: making him laugh, disarming him, was necessarily flirtatious, but it could just as well have been an effect of my happiness, encouraged by the large glass of Rioja.

He had signalled earlier that our lunch was on him but I wished to make a point of my independence, easier since I felt grateful for his intention. So when we called for the bill I made it clear that I intended to pay my share, adding, fishing subtly − I hoped − for information, saying:

− This would become expensive if you invited many ladies...

– No, not at all, this is the only time.

– But you must have scanned the 'Encounters' page?

– No, the words 'Conversation Wanted' caught my eye, that's what did it...

That was good, and I felt gratified at his words. When we got up to leave, he accompanied me home, a short walk away from the underground station. We soon stopped by the black railings outside my flat. I had enjoyed walking with this tall and easy man, and said, as a manner of goodbye, mockingly modest, knowingly provocative:

– Well, Mick, you MAY call me...

– Except I don't have your phone number...!

– Oh, right, let me find a piece of paper...here...

– Ter-rific! he said with a smile, putting it in his pocket.

– That good, eh? I quipped, chuckling, and scolding myself immediately for being so brash.

He laughed and bent down to kiss my cheek.

Once indoors, I quickly poured myself a large glass of cold water to quieten the growing euphoria.

*

Would he ring? When would he ring? Tonight would be too soon, we were supposed to behave sensibly, perhaps tomorrow, a Thursday. There was time, I should allow him to take the initiative, be a Man, albeit an Englishman.... His generation of men could sometimes still be shy, or at least awkward. In the past, David had been initially stilted and self-conscious, before giving in to passion...but David didn't truly like women, or only as long as they resisted him, and had declared to me more than once: "I hate sharing!" At least Mick had made it clear that he needed and wanted to share his life, a huge difference.

But who was Mick? I was, as is my way, intellectually outraged by his incapacity to describe himself. I was sure my daughter would know how to reply: Adam, her boyfriend, obviously knew, who told her recently she should have three initials after her name: G, L, B: Generous, Loving, and Busy! This should be a dinner-party game, I thought. I felt I knew who I was, my only problem had been to restrict my own description in my ad to a few words so as to leave room to describe my desired partner. The limit of twenty-five words rather concentrated your mind!

All evening and the following day, I scolded Mick in my thoughts: if you don't know who you are, are you then defining yourself merely as a set of actions and reactions? Have you never wondered – indeed, been told – what other people thought of you? "Michael is a bright student, unfortunately casual with his studies…"; "Young Mick is making some progress, but seems more inclined to watch the birds than concentrate on his essays…" (Did this describe a future bird-watcher or a womaniser?) "My son is a dilettante and a good-for-nothing!" – "No, dear, don't be harsh, he is only young, he is muddled now but you know he is a gifted child!"

"What makes you so sure of yourself, Mick? Do you think you are a gift to women? Let me tell you you're useless!"; "Darling Mick, I am so lucky to have found you, so strong and kind, so caring, I never dreamt to find someone as wonderful as you – and so sexy!"

What did your wife – your women – say about you, that you thought was right, or wrong and you then protested, corrected them with indignation .What do your daughters think of you, that they told you in anger, or gratitude? What do your clients say of you and your work?

The very first philosophy title I was given in the Upper-Sixth form had been: "Who are you?" It hadn't seemed difficult at all…I immediately poured myself into it: "I am a passionate person without any passions…" describing the disarray I was in but nevertheless knowing my place in it. Having been brought up a Catholic had certainly provided me with many an occasion to ponder, search and at times agonise, as we were at all times prompted to 'examine our consciences': looking for sins seemed to be a favourite activity.

– "Bless me, father, for I have sinned…"

– "Yes, my child, I am listening…"

There was no escape, they had you cornered, for if you hadn't sinned in thought, words, or deed, you must have sinned by omission… . And I used to rack my brains to find a sin that I might have committed – I was well-behaved and didn't dare to swear. So as to satisfy the priest half-hidden by the wooden screen that my kneeling dutifully at the time allocated wasn't a pointless exercise, I hid behind greediness: pastries only came once a week on Sundays but the rest of the week provided enough occasions to sin with chocolates or multi-coloured sweets that melted in your mouth: not waiting for them to dissolve but biting into them to rush the tongue into the sudden creaminess was surely a sin: so at least I knew I was greedy. So, who are you, Mick? You mentioned French rosé wine on the telephone and I definitely heard your relish: you would be forgiven for that.

It had, I suspected, been easier for me than for most to reflect on my supposed existence as mother always seemed to put it into doubt, brushing my tentative thoughts or remarks aside when they suited neither time, place, or her vision of my unessential role in her life, since she only attributed to me and my sister as much existence and usefulness as was required by her needs: we were accessories. By no means unusual in those post-war days, we were children of unthinking and selfish parents who were absorbed and affected by the many traumas of the war, the need to survive and salvage what appeared like order.

No wonder existentialism flourished at the time: it was easy then to feel that existence was accidental, aimless, therefore perhaps unnecessary. With so many hidden enemies to avoid or fight, no wonder I strived to make a small place for myself to start with, as a writer-in-waiting (I had to wait to have things to say) who would initially wait on a artist of talent, my husband Paul, until I decided that a life of subservience didn't appeal and left. Still not knowing what to do with myself I threw myself headlong into a passionate and destructive affair with the above-mentioned David who casually provided me with a much-desired daughter as well as many reasons to discover the whys and wherefores of my life...

Friday came without a call from Mick and I debated whether I should call him first; I was fretting: would I seem too forward? Would he be put off if he preferred to take the initiative? There had been, the night before, a call that my answerphone recorded but which I hadn't been able to retrieve: was it him?

I dialled his number but had to leave a message in his absence.

– Hello Mick, it's Hélène here, it's Friday afternoon, the sky is grey, and I think I'll go and see a film. I wondered if you'd like to come with me? But you're not in so I'll go just the same. Bye.

Was it a mistake? It was only a casual invitation...

Saturday followed and I wondered about my programme for what are usually two long days, however I decided to go to the library after lunch, work is always a balm at moments of crisis or indecision. When the telephone rang on the Sunday morning and I heard Mick's voice – pleasant, apologising for missing my call, but there had been a serious rugby match that day! I laughed:

– Ha! I can see you are still addicted!

– What was your film like?

– Not that great, so it's just as well you weren't free, you mightn't have liked it either, quite well made and acted but just not that interesting...

– What are you doing this weekend? he asked.

– Working, pottering, gardening, do you like gardens?

– Not terribly, I prefer nature left to its own devices...

– But don't you think that wherever we go, apart from some far-away and hostile places, we always interfere with nature, always try to manage it somehow.... It may be a shame but this is what we do...

– Are you free next week?

– Some of it yes, but I'm planning to go to Edinburgh on Monday morning, to see an exhibition, I should be back on Wednesday...

– Are you free on Thursday then?

– Yes, Thursday is fine

– Anything you want to do?

– Well, if the weather is nice, I'd love a walk on the Heath – and why not have lunch at Kenwood?

– That sounds lovely. I'll tell you what, let's ring each other on Thursday morning to see what the weather is like, and we can decide...

I should have been cheerful and keener to go to Edinburgh now that I felt a little wanted, but despondency suddenly overwhelmed me: I didn't want to go on my own, I didn't want to have to do that. Fine to take the train, I loved trains, loved looking out of the window, relishing the ever-changing landscape; arriving would be great fun and finding a hotel probably easy; then walking to the Royal Scottish Academy, spending unlimited time watching the exhibits, good. Having lunch would be fine too, almost anywhere would do, I would need a rest anyway and it would be an opportunity to observe the crowds, the different rhythms. Then the Traverse Gallery, more shows, the old town, a break for tea. After that a certain lassitude would set in, the lack of a person to talk to and exchange with would start to weigh on me, I knew, and there would still be hours before a necessarily short dinner on my own, and too long before bedtime unless I wanted to go to sleep at nine o'clock…that's what I couldn't stand.

At times like these I could easily put myself up for adoption…

I cancelled the trip. Almost immediately, the telephone rang and opportunities appeared out of nowhere, lunch with a friend, dinner with my daughter, and an opportune visit by a neighbour to whom I was only too happy to do a favour: I told him about my aborted trip and he exclaimed:

– But I have a few friends in Edinburgh who would have been delighted to have dinner with you!

So, maybe another time? I quite liked the idea of meeting strangers.

– Arthur, if I ask you the question: 'who are you?' how would you describe yourself? Eight to ten words…

– Ah, well…I don't know…sarcastic, helpful, nice, sincere, slimmish, good cook, er…

– Right! That's not bad! – Not bad for a man of thirty-five!

My daughter, later, on the telephone, obliged fluently as I took notes:

– Loyal, gregarious, demanding, happy, loving, chatty, thoughtful, conscientious, adaptable, busy-thinker…of course some of that I've been told, school reports, that sort of thing…why?

I explained about Mick and she sounded outraged:

– Mu-um! You've only just met him and you give him a philosophy essay title! You're so demanding!

Philosophy should be on the curriculum, as a life skill, I insist, and 'Who are you?' should be the first homework: any child would be happy and intrigued to find out: I am an ogre! I am Mummy's little husband...an astronaut! I am the Queen of Sheba! I am nice...I am sad...

And I wondered to myself: how come someone so demanding found herself such lousy men? Was I setting myself up for disappointment? And could I now avoid what used to be the inevitable? I still felt strongly about the necessity of self-awareness: wasn't knowing oneself an affirmation of who one was?

Chapter Nineteen

The stranger I was meeting today was no longer a real stranger, but he had a lot to prove, mostly that he was nothing like David, and then I would feel that the features he innocently wore could properly be called his own, he would be Mick.

When I looked at the clock, it was eleven-thirty, a little late for a long walk before lunch? As I decided to make the call, his answerphone greeted me:

– Hello, Mick, it's Hélène here, Thursday morning, eleven-ish, the sun is shining and I was wondering if you were still free to meet this morning. Give me a ring when you get back – if you get back.

I was livid. Right. That was that, then. No good. What a waste of time! I felt cold and hard. My daughter had announced her visit the following day so why not go and buy her the chipolatas she wanted me to cook for her, as well as something wicked for dessert? I left promptly. Anger energised me as I walked in the September sunshine.

When I returned and started preparing lunch, an hour and a half later, the telephone rang. It was Mick, and I let him talk to my machine first:

– Hello, Hélène, it's Mick. I've just got back! (Laughter.)

You go out for half-an-hour and get back three and a half hours later!

I picked up the phone:

– What happened?

He explained: a friend whose art exhibition he had helped to arrange had asked him to go and collect his paintings; he thought he would merely have to put them in the back of his car but found that they all had to be individually wrapped, had to go and buy bubble wrap, etc.

– And you didn't have my number? I helped.

– No! – I wished he'd apologised, been aware he'd also messed up my day.

– So what do you suggest? I queried, a little terse.

– Right. Tomorrow is no good, I'm seeing a client, but I am free this weekend, and all of next week except for one day. When are you free?

I explained my daughter would be staying with me on Friday night and some of Saturday, making him laugh about the special order of chipolatas and chocolate pudding, but Sunday was free...

– Fine, let's do Sunday, I'll ring you in the morning, eleven-ish. How was your trip to Edinburgh?

I burst out laughing:

– I'll tell you on Sunday!

Saturday morning greeted me, obviously in anticipation of my date with Mick, with my body shaking me out of a dreamless sleep into magical, pleasurable tremors, and I woke up with a smile for once: a freebee...

My daughter, having stayed overnight, was still asleep after our late night of chatting, so I tiptoed to the bathroom first, then to the kettle, the necessary rituals. I could glance in the distance – the birds know my rhythms – a blackbird perched on the back of a patio chair, another on the grass nearby, waiting for their morning raisins, and didn't resist their expectations; being taken for granted by them was a treat, just as I saw it as a privilege that my daughter relied on me, at least there was no end to that particular joy, and she would soon wake up, with her sleepy baby face...She would be gone soon enough, but not before the chocolate croissants in the orangery with redbush tea, sitting amid the cushions in my winter dressing gown, not until we had talked and confided and laughed for another two hours, when she would decide she had to go in a rush, having lunch with a schoolfriend.

For my own protection, as a safeguard, there was something I needed to do ahead of my meeting with Mick the next day: place a new ad in a different Sunday newspaper. Although I understood it was symptomatic of late summer that there would be some weariness in the mood of the Encounters page, with the same people advertising week after week, it was also the same people who read them, now with a certain tedium. I needed to change my text and rewrote it as follows:

– SPIRITED, warm, attractive French woman, 60, into arts and ideas, WLTM caring, affectionate, fit and solvent man of broad culture for intelligent conversation and more. London.

Half-heartedly accepting that time had passed, at least since I undertook this project, I was now no longer officially in my late fifties, while wondering if I risked attracting an older group of 'applicant': but much older than Bob (early seventies), or Harold (seventy-four and looking as ancient as Methuselah)? Probably not. There wasn't enough room in my ad to specify a man in a desired age range of, say, sixty to sixty-five; including the important location: London, it already came to twenty-six words. Besides, Mick looking my own age didn't bother me in the least, seeing as he seemed fit and relaxed in his manners...

I woke up on Sunday with the strange and joyless feeling that I wouldn't see Michael that day, despite our date, despite the optimistic September sunshine, despite the fact that I found myself standing later in front of my open wardrobe wondering what to wear. I couldn't seem to summon up any enthusiasm: was I already protecting myself against disappointment?

When the telephone rang at eleven-thirty, I made an effort to sound light and joyful:

– Hi, Mick!

– Hello, Hélène, how are you?

– Exhausted after carrying the Sunday papers home, they seem to get heavier every week – and they have a lot to write about today, don't they? (Gordon Brown had been planning a coup, it seemed, the air was thick with half-facts and hypotheses.) It'll take me a week to go through it all!

– Hélène, I'm sorry – he did sound sorry – I won't be able to make it today, I was in the shower when my telephone rang, just now, and it was my ex-wife who wanted me to come round because there's a problem with my daughter...

– You could've given me some warning, I said without thinking, but probably wanting him to feel bad as well.

– It's only just happened, he insisted, I have to go to the house. You do realise, don't you, the problem isn't about my relationship with my daughter, but my wife's...

I was feeling horribly sorry for myself and could barely find the words to sympathise:

– Well, I hope you'll be able to help – I'm sorry too, two cancellations in one week, it's bad luck...

My disappointment was tangible, I didn't care if he knew it.

– All right, Mick, good luck, I'll leave it with you…

I might as well have drawn a large cross over the day, cancelled the day, killed the day, fallen asleep over the papers. Stared at the garden, fallen asleep… . If I didn't get another call from a friend – I had turned down Diana's invitation yesterday to join her on an outing to Richmond, my day would be a washout. I therefore resorted, like many a wounded, unimaginative and rudimentary woman, to a very basic comfort, rushing out to buy myself a large Danish pastry and a packet of chocolate biscuits, which I ate with angry relish: at least, you wouldn't take THAT away from me…

The day had appeared so beautiful, the soft light of a late summer day so inviting for the leisurely pleasure of a stroll on the Heath with a nice man. Mere friendliness would have been fine, I had been dying for so long for a walk 'à deux' into the gracious landscape that I knew so well and which always looked different and entrancing. I might have brought bread for the birds, we would have laughed, sat on the grass… . Lunch at Kenwood – there might have been a long queue but we wouldn't have cared – it would have been so blissful, so civilised. I would have felt lucky, normal…

Fortunately, days became nights, when you could put everything aside, sink into that other world of nothingness, carefree – dead at least for a while.

I decided on the Monday that Mick's given reason for cancelling our date was genuine: he had wished me to know that it wasn't his daughter's relationship with him that was the cause of the problem, but hers with his wife; his ex-wife. He had wanted to reassure me, or at the very least clear himself of any possible blame on my part. Not only was it genuine, it was serious enough for him to have to drop everything and rush to the old family house. I became worried: how bad was it? Had I been sympathetic enough? I hadn't been sympathetic at all! I would ring him to say I hoped it had been nothing very serious and he was no longer worried about his daughter.... Of course I also wanted to maintain contact.

*

The week is slipping slyly away, the days keeping quiet, trying not to be noticed, even though I make vague attempts to get them into some kind of shape. These attempts, however, are half-hearted, lacking in motivation. They pretend, put on smiles, do errands, go for walks...

I called Mick – or rather left a message on his answerphone, last Monday (well over a week ago now) to say I hoped the problem wasn't too serious and he'd managed to solve it. I knew I shouldn't have rung and got told off by a friend ("You've done it again! You mustn't! He is going to think you're chasing him, men don't like that, they want to do the chasing themselves, you'll frighten him! You know what you're like, it's a learning curve for you!")

I said sorry to the Gods even though I have no grounds to look up to them or trust them. They now stand in as an occasional superego, a clear demotion, but still fulfil a useful role.

Anyway, Mick hadn't returned my call and, reluctantly, I had to leave it. The difficulties between his daughter and his ex-wife were obviously serious, they must have had a row and the daughter wished to move out. It could be she had moved in with her father, temporarily, or they have been flat-hunting for her. Still, it was just possible that he would ring me one day...

Half-heartedly, I perused the Sunday papers and listened to the voice of Howard from Beckenham who described himself as a free spirit, young at heart, wanted to meet a free-spirited lady, "easy-come, easy-go" – but no, sorry, Howard, I am not "easy-come, easy-go", I am difficult, fun but demanding, and would like you no more than you would like me...

I distracted myself for a while with other people's requests:

– "Piano man, 32, with nimble fingers and a good ear, seeks mature lady who fancies a jam."

– " Single, Catholic, 44, immaculate past, is seeking a good Catholic pure girl, who can cook well, and who can do all housework, who is also capable of sewing and a good home maker, in order to marry at the soonest opportunity. Personal fortune would be desirable but is not however a precondition."

I read elsewhere that "A widow had pickled her late husband's penis to keep it as a souvenir of their marriage. Uta Schneider, 65, used a butcher's knife to remove the privates from a hospital in Stuttgart, Germany. "It was his best asset and gave me so much pleasure," said Uta, married for 35 years. "I wanted to pickle it for eternity. It's what he would have wished."

Love is everywhere...

Chapter Twenty

I felt horribly lonely over the days that followed, didn't seem to know what to do with myself, tried to find diversions to kill time, like going to see films in the afternoon, which shortened the demands of the daylight hours. The evenings were preordained, with their chain of news programmes that I had at least an interest in; later, I would cook dinner, eat it on a tray in front of the television, and perhaps the telephone would ring, a friend would want news and a chat, a welcome intrusion.

That's how it goes...I was very hurt and puzzled in the absence of a call from Mick. I couldn't understand how a man would had asked to see me again, had made arrangements for our dates had seemed to disappear from the face of the earth. I may have frightened him by calling him more often than was necessary. I may have intimidated him with my mischievous questioning: "Who are you, Mick?" (but I was having impish fun imagining him pacing the streets of North London holding his head in his hands in despair like the person in Munch's *Scream* painting, the prey of agonising existential torment, forever tortured by the question: "Who am I?") It could also be that the problems between his daughter and ex-wife had revived his own past difficulties with the latter, – or might I have reminded him of her? I would never know. That is what I found the most unnerving and disorienting: there was no explanation, no ending, no closure. Knowing that I had been at fault in some way would have been easier to take, because he would have been entitled to his reaction. As it was, I was myself left in a vacuum, mere flotsam.

Thinking of going for a walk to the park was as much an ordeal as it might have provided relief, for it meant confronting a world made of crowds, groups, families, or worse: couples, emphasising my solitude as well as my difference and alienation. I frequently chose to stay in and feigned sleep, a good place to hide…

When I came out of that particular torpor, I thought that I might put my personal ad back in the Saturday *Times*, where I had started my quest: I considered altering it slightly: I had been getting very few replies of late, although this could have been a seasonal effect, but could it be that some men were put off at first at the thought of a foreigner, a French woman? I could well see that that could be the case: I had no problems myself with Englishmen, knowing them well through having lived in London for so long (far longer by now than I had lived in France) or Americans possibly, but I wouldn't necessarily choose to meet a man of another nationality: why add to the differences already there, and to the ones due to our gender? Restricted by the number of words, I reflected that if I dropped 'French' from my text, I could replace it with 'interesting' as an added attribute of the man requested, since not all intelligent men were necessarily interesting at all? (The word 'self-aware' also came to mind after my experience with Mick.) I could then include the word 'French' in my voice message where it would be in the company of many more describing me, my tastes, occupations, and wishes, and it wouldn't stand out quite so much. Beforehand, though, I would call my voice box one last time just in case there was a late message, you never knew.

A strong, assertive male voice greeted me, and I listened rather stunned, for its message started with: 'I LOVE YOUR COUNTRY!' immediately contradicting my previous intention. He adored French culture, naming Camus, Sartre, Flaubert, 'and the wonderful Voltaire!' with enthusiasm. Its painters, its artists and stars: Jeanne Moreau, Gerard Depardieu.... He had motored many times through France. He had been an entrepreneur, worked in show business, journalism, had written comedies, and was now chairman of an important company. He would be sixty-seven in December. 'The love of my life,' he added, 'died earlier this year, and I haven't yet met any woman I was interested in. I was thinking of putting an ad in 'Soulmates' starting with: "French woman preferred"!!' His name was Owen and he left his mobile number.

Astounded and bewildered, I sat looking ahead in a daze, the telephone still close to my ear long after he had stopped talking.

*

I rang him back three days later and he returned my call promptly: friendly, energetic, articulate, Owen was open and clear about his life as well as with the terrible loss of his wife earlier on in the year (we are in October, I thought, it could only be six months or so, but don't they say that people who have been happily married are very quick to marry again? Is it because they know how to be happy, they 'know how to deal with' love, I wondered – remembering the phrase by Anita Brookner that had so struck me a while ago, and could I talk about her books with this man?) He was movingly candid about his wife:

"We had been married for four years, although we had been together twenty-two years – our affair started while I was still married to my first wife, who was unwell, you know, I only left when the children were older. We did everything together, there were a lot of hugs and kisses, lots of laughing... . We were very tactile. You know what Spike Milligan said, that there are two sorts of people, the 'touchers' and the 'non-touchers', she was lovely, very lively and warm..."

– A hard act to follow...I commented gently, thinking: this man knows how to love.

– I am not trying to replace her, you just can't. But I feel more and more that life is for sharing, you want someone compatible and loving to share, life is meaningless without it. She was a very good business partner too, we set up the business together and have done very well. It wasn't always like that of course, we had hairy beginnings in the eighties when business was so bad – I was in the newspaper industry then, and revenue was falling because people no longer advertised...so I know about being poor as well...

When he asked about me – I was aware of a complicated and painful life, and had to simplify a great deal: brought up in post-war provincial France by narrow-minded and demanding parents, university in Bordeaux, later married an Englishman who was an art teacher and a very good painter... . Then I met someone else and I had one daughter after losing a first baby who was still-born (I realise this is the first time I talk of this to a stranger), a long time ago now...I could tell he was listening attentively. He went to France a great deal, Nice particularly, there was this hotel where he always had the same room, with a corner view, he could see the whole bay from his bed.

– Do you know people there?

– We went to restaurants a lot, you know, so I know a lot of restaurant owners, and I talk to them in my silly restaurant French! he laughed. Do you know Nice?

– No, I don't, in fact I don't know the Côte d'Azur at all, my family was in the South-West, you see, so there was no opportunity, and then I was a single parent – and I could weep at this point because I am now feeling so deprived, all these people, these foreigners, they know my country so much better than I do, they even buy places there...

– So maybe I could introduce you to it sometime...

– That's a few steps away from where we are now! I exclaimed in surprise.

We laughed. Laughter was so companionable. Laughter was kind.

– So what do you do now? (For he is the kind of man who can't imagine not doing anything, I can hear it in his voice.)

– Well, I write, as I said. I go to the local library a few times a week to work, it's the best way, there are all these Asian students and they are so serious, so quiet, it's wonderful, you can't do anything but work hard as well. I go to the cinema sometimes, not the theatre because I prefer to have someone with me, I go to art galleries, for walks...

– You need to get out more! Anyway, we are going to meet, aren't we?

– Yes, that would be very nice. But tell me, what do you look like?

– Well, as I've said, I think, I'm six foot tall. I have been described by women as 'charming' but that's not the same as 'good-looking, is it? (laughter). My hair is at the front, I'm bald at the back...

– So you're back to front!

More laughter.

– How do you keep fit? I asked, preferring to assume that he did, since it is one of my 'requirements'.

– Oh, I walk, I like walking around the town, looking at the architecture; I go on safaris… . Now, I know you're five foot two, blonde with blue eyes, are you quite slim?

– Reasonably…

– And how old are you?

(I did say…I'm sixty.)

– Sixty-seven.

(There, it's done, I'm sick of telling tales. I want to be me, but know it can be costly)

– Oh, just like me…

*

'Serendipity' is a word I like. The thing itself can be totally disarming in its intemperate mischief, cancelling out any preconceptions and plans as well as expectations, for it seems I was right, if only in this instance, to have declared myself as French in my ad. There are, in my mind's eye – nowadays both the sharper and the more unreliable one – images of a loving and kindly man, obviously well-off, who has the time and inclination to take me travelling around my long-lost country. I pray to him: 'Give me my country back!', and he does, we go everywhere, we may even buy a small place in some village, depending on finances: I would be quite happy with a small flat; with two bedrooms, so I may take my daughter and her boyfriend as well on occasion, or a friend…

Owen suggested that we meet in the entrance hall of Tate Britain at twelve-thirty the next Saturday, 'we'll have lunch at the restaurant there, they've a very good wine list'. That was only two days away now. I was looking forward to meeting him, knowing there would be no shortage of conversation. I hoped the weather would be nice as I would prefer not to arrive wet. What would I wear? Skirt or trousers? My daughter wisely advised me to wear what I am most comfortable with: that would be trousers. However a skirt was what I felt most feminine in, though slightly vulnerable, and mine are long enough to hide my fat legs. Heels will be a must. A short jacket. A long scarf would be elegant, I felt feminine and wanted to look it.

For the first time in over a decade, I bought *Elle* magazine, partly because it had a special offer of a singlet t-shirt which would make me feel young and upbeat, and I reacquainted myself with the long-lost thrill of thumbing through the pages of fashion and glamour, now the province of the young and beautiful. Yes, I would wear a bright lipstick.

I bumped into a neighbour and had to stop myself telling her: 'I've got a date!' which would've been totally out of place as I hardly know her. I carefully shaved my legs and pulled a couple of hairs off my chin, found a good pair of grey tights to tone in with my outfit and felt quite special: I hadn't worn a skirt for ages and this one was wide and flouncy and danced as I walked. Among the mail that came through the door that morning was a small catalogue of 'Presents for Men', which could solve a few problems as choosing for a man can be so problematic, not that I knew many – but if Owen and I got on well, you never knew, it might be useful…I enjoy buying presents for a man.

As I waited on a well-placed chair in the entrance hall of Tate Britain, and faced a huge and intimidating cardboard cut out of Henry VIII – the Holbein exhibition was on – I looked at the King's mean face and prayed that I would like Owen a little.

Soon an elderly gentleman rushed towards me with his right hand outstretched, asking:

– Are you Hélène?

Wondering whether to feel resigned once again (Owen looked very much his age – my age) but determined to be positive, I smiled and replied:

– Yes, I am.

– I thought you must be, you look so French, so elegant!

– Thank you. (I silently thanked Marks and Spencer for my skirt and top.)

We were making our way towards the restaurant, a delightful room decorated with an all-round mural of foliage. Owen had booked what must be his favourite table, the corner one near the entrance, which made conversation companionable as we would be sitting half-facing and half next to each other, providing a certain degree of intimacy. The menu was more expensive than I wished, but I was prepared to pay my share, such an occasion happened only too rarely. On the other hand, Owen seemed a gentleman in the old mould, he might insist on paying the bill. He looked very much like the cultured businessman he was, there was a smoothness about him, and a courteousness which made him appear solicitous and anxious to please. The skin of his cheeks was dry and smooth, giving them a parchment-like appearance. His teeth, on narrow gums, were very unattractive, being fairly long and yellow, but his eyes were lively behind his glasses and he proved animated and laughed easily. The nose, somewhat sharp and beaky, would lend itself to caricature I thought, but his hands were long-fingered and fine.

The service was prompt and efficient and he seemed well-known to the head-waitress, chatting with her amicably. He turned to me:

– Will you have some wine?

– I don't normally drink at lunchtime, it makes me sleepy, but I might have a small glass this time?

– We'll have a half-bottle, he decided, choosing with authority a delicious Burgundy.

He had started his career as a journalist in the local press, finally becoming editor, later acquiring several newspapers. However, the economic downturn that the country suffered in the late eighties under Thatcher made things extremely hard, to the point where he had to ask his bank for an unsecured loan, 'which would be impossible nowadays'. It became urgent to change direction and his own business slowly took shape. What about me? Well, I had myself taken Media Studies while at university, saving me from a lifetime of teaching in France that a literature degree would have condemned me to. Unfortunately, I had to fall back onto teaching when I came to England, particularly when my English husband decided without telling me to be a full-time artist, obliging me as the sole earner to give private lessons as well so we could make ends meet. (I was very obliging in those days...) I later had a child with a nasty man. As well as writing a book, I had written poetry for years and had some fifteen poems published in good poetry magazines:

– I'd love to read some...

Of course he talked about his wife and I didn't expect him not to, I actually liked the way he spoke about her, lovingly and simply, showing his heart, and he made me laugh by telling me how she seduced him, at that time an occasional business acquaintance:

– In the street! She kissed me in the street! She said that if that was the last time we met, she couldn't miss that opportunity! And we've been together ever since. We were lovers a long time, twenty-two years, only got married four years ago... . We were very tactile – couldn't take our hands off each other – lots of cuddles...and we did everything together... . You know, men are stupid, we think we know about women but we don't: we do our bit and we think the woman is pleased, and that's not true at all! When I was young, of course we did everything to get girls into bed, and sometimes succeeded, and we thought that's all there was to it! I was lucky to have been taken in hand by an older woman – she must have been twenty-five – who showed me how to please a woman. Most men don't know, because no one tells them...

– You have the internet nowadays, I suggested. (Was I feeling slightly uncomfortable?)

– I hope you don't mind me talking to you like this, but it's true, he added, pressing his hand warmly on mine, men are silly. My wife and I started the business together you know, I couldn't have done it without her, and you should've seen us argue in the boardroom, people were horrified, but it didn't matter at all because we were...

– Safe.

– Exactly. He smiled at me.

– Have you put an ad in the newspapers yourself? I queried.

– Yes, I have, a while back...

– What did your ad say?

– Oh, I don't know, something like: 'Loving and sharing is what matters...' Something like that. I had eighty replies.

– What? I was astounded.

– Yes, there were no end of women telling me their problems, how unhappy they were...how much they needed a man to lean on...I narrowed it down to twenty and rang about ten. You don't want someone collapsing on you, you want someone independent...

– I am amazed! I only got one reply last week, and it was you...I think it was a bad time of the year because the Soulmates page people were offering me a slot next weekend, and the weekend after, and the following one.

Maybe it's the age also, and possibly not everyone wants a Frenchwoman? Have you met many women?

– A few. There was this woman I liked, a businesswoman, high-powered, very successful. I showed her the house. I took her to Nice – you know, her own room. Bought her lots of clothes…At the end she said she couldn't, and do you know, at that moment I stopped desiring her, it was over… . Have you met many men?

– Not many at all. You know, often a telephone conversation is enough for you to decide you do not want to meet that person. And when you do, well, I can fall back on the fact that I work most afternoons in the library, I say I must go and do some work…

– So I take it you aren't working today? he asked with a grin.

– No, not today, today is a nice day, I smiled. I met someone I liked recently, but he got totally lost when I asked him to describe himself to me. And I thought: you are in your sixties, you have been educated, got jobs, been a boss even, were married, had children, got divorced, and you can't say who you are? But I liked him. We arranged to meet again a couple of times, but each time he seemed to have a very valid reason to cancel, and then he disappeared… .Very puzzling. Because it felt like rejection, and so it was hard to take, particularly when you don't know the reason…

– Yes, rejection is hard for a woman. Men are used to it, it's easier for us…

We were still sitting at the table, companionably. There was something like friendship, a fellowship between us: we knew about the world, about pain, about love. He had been by far the luckier one. When he had asked me if I'd had a fulfilling relationship with a man, I had to admit: no, I haven't.

– You see, I continued, it's often a question of development: you are brought up by parents who perhaps are not fulfilled, are difficult in some way, a lot of that can hold you back, and I was such a late developer! There was this phrase in a book by Anita Brookner – do you know her books?

– Yes, my wife used to like her, but I think she's a women's writer…

– Well, she says in this book, talking about the heroine: "She realised that love was available to those who knew how to deal with it." I thought that was so profound, so true. And I think perhaps I wasn't the kind of person who knew how to deal with it in the past, and I made the wrong choices…

Then we talked of our children, his two boys and one girl: the older one is doing very well in the family business and his daughter is introducing him tomorrow to her new boyfriend, hopefully an improvement on the previous one; she has an eight-year-old daughter, his only grandchild, delightful; she will be bringing the food and cook the meal at his house. She knows about me, he had said to her: "I am meeting this French woman today, and she wants me to report back. You'll meet her."

I chuckled, adding that my daughter also wanted to know about him tonight; she worried about me, even had a nightmare the other day and woke her boyfriend up in tears: apparently, I was sleeping with all these men, and now I was pregnant! I said to her: "My darling, I can promise you solemnly that I will NOT get pregnant!" and we were in stitches… . He roared with laughter.

He told me stories me about his travels in France, the best hotels:

– It sounds wonderful, but it's easy when you have money, I exclaim.

– My dear, he laughed, I don't have money, I have MILLIONS!

I raised my eyes to the ceiling, comically, then put on a stern face and scolded him:

– You mustn't say that to everyone! Some women, you know, they would take advantage…

– I give huge amounts to charity of course, Victims of Torture and others…you've got to.

Our meal was over and he asked for the bill. I leant towards him:

– I normally pay my share, but I can see it's not your style…

He pulled a wad of cash out of his trousers pocket:

– I like cash, he grinned.

– Me too, that's what I think when I go to the cash point…

We burst out laughing.

When we looked at the river from the vantage point of the top of the steps outside Tate Britain the sun was still shining and even warm, giving the day an extra air of privilege.

– Shall we have a walk? he proposed.

– Yes, certainly, it's such a lovely day.

As we were about to walk down the steps, he took hold of my hand.

– Hand in hand?

– This is too early, I said, withdrawing it.

He seemed to take it with good grace: as he said, men are used to rejection, and this was a mild one. There may be more. I was obscurely aware, without altogether formulating it to myself, that Owen was a fast mover, which often goes with being used to good things. He had made sure – was it conscious? – that I understood he knew how to pleasure a woman, which felt intrusive and premature to say the least, and that he was very rich. This was compensated for by the fact that he was a good, fun, kind-hearted man of genuine feelings and I appreciated the spontaneity of his friendliness. I decided not to be intimidated, it would have been in bad grace not to enjoy the day: we were both hungry for company and today at least, we were lucky.

– Have you ever been on the Tate-to-Tate boat? I enquired as the embarkation point came into view.

– No, never. Would you like to go on it?

– Oh, yes, it's lovely you know, you go straight to Tate Modern, it only takes twenty minutes and the sights are great, you'll like it. And we could walk back on the other side…

– All right then, let's go.

He seemed to enjoy the ride, looking amused. I certainly did. When our turn came to pay, I dutifully showed my Freedom Pass and he looked at me jovially:

– So you're not going to cost me too much this time.

– That's right…

We settled down to the ride. He was humming gently, which gave me a thrill of pleasure: I was grateful to Owen for being content in my company.

– You see there? he pointed to our left. That's the Savoy. I have a room there for when I want to stay overnight, with a view on the river…

We disembarked soon after.

– Have you ever been to the Globe? I enquired as we faced the entrance to the theatre.

– No, I haven't.

– Come and have a look at the gate, I beckoned, it's one of my favourite things, covered with all sorts of animals, birds and insects, gorgeous…

He agreed it was beautiful, and we started on our walk

westwards along the river. The gentle autumn sun, accompanied by a soft breeze, was shining on both banks, encouraging a leisurely walk. We were silent for a while.

– Would you like a drink?

We had reached the South Bank Centre and a few tables outside proved inviting.

– Yes – oh dear! you didn't have your coffee at the restaurant!

He laughed:

– It doesn't matter, I wanted a walk; I can have it now.

We sipped our drinks slowly, making sure we kept sitting in the lowering sun, moving our chairs accordingly. Noticing Owen's frequent sidelong glances towards me, I became aware of the lacy vest under my top having slipped, revealing more than was intended of my cleavage, and pulled it up.

We soon reached the second-hand book stalls outside Queen Elizabeth Hall. Owen had already told me that he collected first editions, he would be interested to look, and I certainly was keen to browse. We winded our way separately and haphazardly among the rows of books, when he came to me with a hardback in his hand:

– You know Julian Barnes?

– I certainly know of him, he wrote *Flaubert's Parrot*, didn't he?

– Yes, excellent writer, I'll get this for you, you'll enjoy it.

The book in question was: *Cross Channel*, and knowing of Barnes's love of France, I knew I would. I thanked Owen warmly: the man had a gentle touch, a gentle heart. I decided to find a book to give him too, and carried on searching for a while, until I found an English translation of *Therese* by Francois Mauriac, and rushed towards him:

– I've got something for you too: you know Mauriac, don't you?

– Of course.

– This is the story of a woman, in provincial France, in the thirties; maybe you know how stultifying life in the provinces could be. It's horrible…

We laughed: I was giving a horrible book.

– I used to think I nearly was Thérèse Desqueyroux myself – but I escaped! I think you'll like it, it's a terrific story.

I was glad to have found a small present for him, which made our relationship a little more even.

When we set about to cross Westminster Bridge, the sun was still there over the top of the roofs, causing long and elegant shadows. I was feeling very tired and wanted nothing more than lie quietly on my living-room couch with a newspaper and a cup of tea. I wondered if Owen was also tired. There seemed to be a natural end to our meeting when he asked how I would be getting home:

– Oh, easily from here. I can get the 24 bus near the Houses of Parliament, it goes to Hampstead Heath. It'll be leisurely. I used to take it from here a few years ago when I did jury service at the Law Courts over there. I pointed to the beautiful buildings of lacy stonework in the distance. And you? Did you come by car, where did you park?

– Oh, I have a driver, I can ring him anytime, he won't be long.

– Really? Where is he?

– I don't know, but he won't be very long.

I felt a little mischievous:

–You know what you could do? You could have a chip implanted and he could follow you all over London!

He chuckled – and suddenly I was panicking as a no 24 came into view. I shouted, 'My bus!' quickly stretched towards Owen to kiss his cheek before I started running to catch the bus. I turned around briefly and we both gestured that we would ring each other. I caught the bus just in time and as I settled down in my seat immediately regretted having left Owen in such a hurry: surely I could have waited for the next one? Did it look as if I was running away?

When I finally reached my flat an hour later I was overwhelmed with exhaustion: it was barely six o'clock and we had walked a good deal but in a leisurely fashion, and I wasn't that unfit. It had been, though, an emotionally demanding day, as all the features of the 'exercise' Owen and I were engaged in had come into play, crammed into a few hours: did we like the look of one another? were we companionable? were we suitable intellectually, emotionally? was there a frisson of attraction? It was as if we were summoned by the nature of our meeting to answer immediately all these questions under penalty of.... of what? having to cope with embarrassment – as if a second meeting would tie us too much to each other and make a subsequent break a fearful prospect. When some of the elements for success were present: a feeling of kinship, a social and intellectual match, physical attraction or at least the possibility that it might develop, we were under huge pressure to feel, judge and decide promptly. Any other social circumstances would have allowed us infinitely more leeway and time to be and play, without the terrifying responsibility of knowing that each of us was engaged in that vital pursuit of finding a mate and that that first meeting was the only chance. Like a gambler at the games table we might have everything to gain – or everything to lose. The tension was near unbearable. I was also under the pressure of seeing a relationship with Owen as a solution for accomplishing my deepest wishes: this man loved France, it would therefore be easy to visit frequently, maybe to buy a house there: I would have the French home for which I had yearned for so long. I could help my daughter buy a flat. I could have private health insurance, I could have raspberries every day at breakfast…and if his children liked me I could have a new family…

Not everyone need be so intense, but how did you avoid anguish if you were emotionally sensitive, understanding what was at stake and serious about finding a suitable partner? Of course few of the people one met would provoke any conflicts if they failed to arouse interest: one would just have to be philosophical, exercise tolerance, show some patience and kindness; but the stakes, in this quest, were always high, the hopes at times immense and unreasonable, at the same time we had to be aware that the chances of success were very low. One heard, of course, of happy couples who had met that way, one clung to the slightest hope, particularly if the initial telephone contact had proved promising. It seemed, if the response that Owen had received to his ad was anything to go by – eighty replies! – that men would be luckier than women, they simply had more choice: women wrote more because they were more expansive, less timorous, and more carried by the hope of romance. It could also be that older men were also less available because they had begun to suffer ill-health. Strong women like me had better remain strong, for it wouldn't be easy.

The following day was a Sunday, when Owen was due to have lunch with his daughter and meet her new boyfriend. He would be at home reading the Sunday papers no doubt. I wanted to apologise for such a quick exit the day before, and rang his mobile where I had to leave a message. Five minutes later he was ringing me back and I found myself saying a friendly but strangely intimate: 'Hello!' He seemed pleased to hear from me.

– Owen, I just wanted to apologise for running away like that yesterday, what you saw was a Pavlovian reflex of Woman Seeing Her Bus! I could've waited for the next one...

– No, not at all, don't worry, in fact the weather was so nice I decided to walk to Victoria...

– Anyway, I know you are seeing your daughter today, so I won't keep you, I just wanted to say sorry. Have a lovely day...

I liked Owen-the-person very much. He was intelligent, had exhibited warmth and charm, and his lifestyle was to say the least attractive. He had seemed to like me, unless he liked to hold hands with any female who came his way. When he had alluded to my possibly meeting his daughter, I hadn't responded. Someone else might have said, 'I'd love to meet her,' showing a liking of Owen-the-man that I couldn't summon at this stage. Might in the future. But might not. I didn't feel at all attracted by him physically, but knew that these things could grow, it was a question of establishing a friendship, warmth, it could take time. Would we give ourselves the time?

Owen had suggested – on the telephone, without having met me! – that he might be the man to take me to Nice: he was, I could see, suffering greatly from emotional deprivation. The death of his wife had left a huge void, and it was so unbearable to this warm and gentle man that he was panicking at the emptiness in front of him: he needed a woman, quickly, desperately, he didn't know how to live any other way. There had been that other woman whom he invited to stay in Nice with him – in her own room, he had indicated, to show that she wasn't under pressure to sleep with him: but she was, of course, since it was all over when she said no... . His need of intimacy was huge and was causing him to behave out of place and out of time, he was in a hurry, he wanted everything now, the hand, the cuddles, the sex...he wanted to stop feeling so wretched.

I wanted to stop feeling so wretched too. I was sick of spending most of my evenings at home, of having no one to talk to, no one knowing I existed and caring who I was and what I was doing. Sick of having no holidays because I had no one to go with and little money – thanks to Emmanuel – to go anywhere interesting. I was appalled at being so under-used, so ignored, so unseen: I had a lot to give and I wanted to share. I needed someone to love who would love me. I was a fish mistakenly imprisoned in a glass bowl when it yearned to swim in the big ocean. And I was tired of meeting men this way as well: we seemed to be like ships passing in the night, looking each other over briefly, then sailing on, making few waves in one another's lives.

Writing was of necessity keeping me isolated, there was little interaction with other adults. My involvement with the Lib Dems was occasional and superficial and I had become too blasé about political engagement to take it any deeper. My friends had their own lives, busy with their occupations, grandchildren, and the younger ones their jobs. I had re-joined the gym where I planned to go three mornings a week. Interested in the law, I enquired about training to be a Justice of the Peace to find out I was 'too old' for it. An informed acquaintance I had approached regarding possibly becoming a Witness Protection Officer hadn't got back to me; as she has two young children I doubted she remembered. I couldn't stand being so invisible. It wasn't the responsibility of my daughter, busy herself with a full-time job and a partner, to fill that gap: we talked most days on the telephone and saw each other regularly but she had her own life, which was how it should be.

The feminist angle – a woman is a whole human being and doesn't depend on a man for self-definition – I thought valid to some degree but I didn't accept any diktat regarding the nature of my personal fulfilment: I deeply believed that we were in this world in order to learn how to love, to love properly, with a generous heart, and the ability to exercise it was an opportunity for growth. I debated these points with the occasional friend, but the solution was mine, though the Gods seemed to insist it was theirs. All I could do was continue in my search, hoping that one day they would be clement. I renewed my ad in the *Observer* for the following weekend with an additional one in the *Guardian*, put a slightly different one in the Saturday *Times* (I was back to 'Conversation wanted'). I called the occasional voicemail to listen to unpromising messages, and had a couple of tedious though short conversations on the telephone: where are the good men? Are they swamped with good women?

However, I felt I hadn't finished my own conversation with Owen: I wanted to talk to him – I was a counsellor after all – about grief and bereavement and could advise him as a friend to bear his pain with patience, not to rush into relationships in panic and anguish, to talk to someone about his wife, to make new friends perhaps. I could be his friend if he wanted: I had a poetry book with my latest published poem to give him as well as an article from *The Times* by a neuro-psychiatrist about the possibility of consciousness after death which might help him think differently about his wife's. I wanted to say: could we meet in a relaxed way this time, as people, without pressure, and to enjoy a bit of friendly contact and conversation? Could we give ourselves a break for a while? Would he like to come and have tea?

But maybe not.

Chapter Twenty-one

The trees were still green in and around the garden: they hung on to their leaves as if they had lost all track of time, ignorant that we had reached the end of October. It didn't used to be like this: many years ago now, expressing her disarray about life and no doubt mourning the unkept promises of the past, my mother had told me: "I am only ever sure of one thing now, and that is the seasons." She couldn't even be certain of that nowadays and I was glad she was no longer here to see the capricious and threatening deregulation of our planet. Myself I found it disorienting; I needed some certainties, the constancy of a human presence at least, even though it would, like me, age and eventually die: we were seasonal beings.

The city itself offered predictable solace: the cinemas I went to for a dream or a thrill, the wonder of a Tennessee Williams play on a Wednesday afternoon, the museums and art Galleries that filled my eyes with lasting beauty: but it would all feel so much richer if I could share it all with someone.

I felt morose.My voice boxes had remained empty this week: why? Still I perused the Soulmates and Encounters pages, left a message that remained unanswered. I was exhausted, but knew that giving up wasn't an option, I might as well erase my own life. I dialled a voice box number and listened: it wasn't so much the voice that was pleasant as its liveliness: the animation that came across was that of a friend talking, a man unencumbered by formality; there was a directness and a matter-of-factness there, as well as a lack of pretension. I left a message just in case.

*

When the telephone, later the same evening, interrupted my melancholy thoughts, it was an unexpected call, a French cousin from whom I hadn't heard for many months: I'm calling you, she said, because a man called Jean-Claude B. has rung me, he's been trying to trace you for quite a while after having been sent from pillar to post. Do you know him?

– Oh, yes, I replied, we were at school together. How bizarre!

– Well, he wishes to contact you: what do you want me to do?

– Hmm…give him my address but not my telephone number, it's easier to deal with that way, you never know…

– That's what I was thinking…so you remember him?

– Oh, yes, we called him Johnny then, for some reason…maybe he's trying to contact the whole class of 1957! Who knows…

I knew better of course, and the smile on my face at that moment was part amusement and part grimace: childhood dies hard. In fact, childhood never dies, it merely feigns sleep, childhood is death-resistant. And if I shuddered, it wasn't because I had come to any harm through Johnny, for I hadn't, but because he had transgressed my decree that some things should remain old history; redundant.

I thought: maybe Johnny is at a loss, maybe the ground isn't too stable under his feet again, and he is reaching out for what seemed good in the past, and if he can reach me again it will be, strangely, as if our story had continued. But it hasn't. Not for me, it was never that important for me.

What flashed through my mind was the memory of him walking in the street, aged eighteen, in a loose, carefree way; he seemed to carry freedom with him in his pockets, in his air of mocking defiance, in his hungry mouth, a young man who would rather kiss than behave: I'm untamed, he seemed to say, I am wild, I smell of hay... . He did, too, as I recalled, and of old wool that has known rain, adding to a tantalizing scent of young male...

He had dropped out of school and wasn't doing anything in particular, while I was in the sixth form preparing for the Baccalaureat. I caught sight of him in town – a small town that reeked of old – and he looked alive, while the rest of us remained, obediently, properly, on the rails. Johnny was handsome in a bad-boy sort of way, which he cultivated and appealed to me in as much as I dared distance myself from my roots, my class, my parents. There were surreptitious and hasty meetings behind the church, in the entrance of the only cinema; there were heady kisses: he tasted so good... . We soon graduated to country lanes, embraced against trees, behind bushes, and on hot summer days rolled in the grass. I remember it well, we were dizzy with lust. When he brought his guitar, we sang songs, and sheltered in a barn when it rained. It is a witness to both my fears and my upbringing that I retained my virginity. One day, I stopped dead in front of a chalk drawing on the wooden barn door of a clumsy flower with vertical petals, slightly reminiscent of an elongated orchid, which intrigued me because it looked at once odd and intimate. I couldn't figure it out. Only later, late one night, when my hand dared at last to go in search of the secret and warm centre of me did I understand the mysterious bloom …

Two or three years passed, and back home on holiday from university, I came across Johnny one morning in my home town: I was pleased to see him, wanted news, stories – wondered if I could smell his smell again – but Johnny, as we both leant against a balustrade overlooking public gardens, Johnny was crying: he had just returned from doing two years' military service in Algeria in the French army: "You can't imagine what they made me do…" He looked exhausted. He had kept on him throughout a photograph he had cut out from a magazine of the eyes of a famous singer, Line Renaud, "because she has your eyes, and I looked at it every day while I was there, thinking of you…"

I saw Johnny briefly a couple more times over the years. He had married, had a child, been divorced. He had also worked in advertising in Paris during which time, having found me by writing at my parents', he rang me in London every evening, at length and at great cost to his firm, over many weeks. As I was alone at the time, these chats, which on reflection bordered on the obsessive, I took as a diversion. I had myself lived in London for years by then, got married and divorced as well.

So much time had passed now: did I really want to renew a link with the past which mattered little now except as a distant memory, though it appeared to matter to him? Even though there seemed to be a nugget of gold in it, a nugget of love? I was not, after all, seeking nuggets.

*

I woke up with a start this morning after a night which I interrupted between five and six o'clock to hear the results of the American Congressional elections. I had fallen asleep afterwards, dreaming confusedly that I was in the middle of a group of Americans and couldn't find my belongings. Jumping out of bed and standing in front of the mirror before I could properly open my eyes, I barely recognised my face: with folds of bitterness creasing my cheeks and my mouth twisted, I looked like a disappointed newborn...

I wanted to be elsewhere, out of here, beyond this time. I wanted to be walking on some mountain with a good man, stop high up and share the sights, in silence for there would be too much to say, it would be so beautiful, so perfect.

*

When I got home, after a late walk, there was a new message on my answering-machine:

– What's all this about, 'Conversation wanted'? I thought all women ever did was talk-talk-talk! Anyway, my name is Liam, I live in Cambridgeshire. I'm trying very hard to be a photographer at the moment and so I come to London a lot. Of course I'm no good at conversation, I stammer, have no sense of humour and I'm a horrible person who hates books, enjoys the war in Iraq, loves Saddam Hussein, and I'm not at all in touch with my feelings...I'm also an Irish graduate aged sixty-two with a daughter and four grandchildren. I was very interested in your ad and in what you say about yourself, so maybe you'll give me a ring?

Chapter Twenty-two

I had barely felt like listening to my voicemail lately, so bleak had been the latest 'crop': a dreary 'applicant' had little to say save that he liked the style of my ad; a second one excitedly exclaimed: 'Hélène! What a lovely description! I would like to talk to you! Call me!' without giving any details about himself. Another, who initially seemed to have some credentials, being a member of the British Film Industry and organising showings and conferences all over the country, talked in a monotone and exclusively about himself: his voice was almost robotic, there was little sign of life on his planet.

After talking briefly on the telephone with the latter, I deleted them all. There was a certain satisfaction in deleting the unwelcome messages, as if one was 'zapping' the authors out of existence in some grown-up computer game. At times no one was left standing, and I would then myself die of boredom...

At least the Irishman who rang recently rang sounded alive! What did he say his name was? Liam? I would ring him back.

– Hello, is that Liam?

– Yes.

– My name is Hélène, you left a message for me in my voice box…

– Oh, yes, hello Hélène, it's very nice to hear from you…

The easy friendliness, the casual warmth, the brotherliness, they were all uniquely Liam: yes, he was presently working as a photographer, coming regularly to London where the jobs were.

– What jobs?

– Oh, parties, celebrations, clubs…people like to buy pictures of themselves partying.

– Where do you live?

– In Cambridgeshire, outside Ely.

– Oh, Ely, it's a lovely town, marvellous cathedral…I did a detour once on my way to Norfolk, just to visit it, it looked wonderful.

– Yes, that's true, it's very beautiful. Where do you live, Hélène?

– In Camden, near Haverstock Hill, a nice flat, with a garden, squirrels and birds. But Liam, I thought you were retired, is photography your hobby?

– Not my hobby, but my passion, I thought it was about time I did what I loved…. And a pension isn't much, I am sixty-two and there's plenty of life left in me…I have a partner, when she is good she's very good, we work well together.

– Do you have children?

– I have one daughter, and four grandchildren. They live in Lincolnshire, on a farm, right in the middle of the countryside. She's lovely, my daughter, and a good mum, she brings up her children well, and they're lovely kids, except the little one is going to have an open-heart operation soon, and we don't know if he'll live or die…

– Oh, my god, that's awful, how is she coping?

– As well as possible, her husband is strong too, but it's hard.

– Yes, I understand you know, I had a still-born baby myself before I had my daughter…

– Oh, really, Hélène, so you've been there too…poor you…

– But my daughter is great, you know, the light of my life, and she's got this lovely boyfriend, they met some years ago at university, they've been living together a while, I see her regularly. Have you been on your own long?

– A few years now. One day my wife decided she didn't want to be married to me any more. She asked her sons to come round – her sons from a previous marriage – and she told me to leave the house. So I left, I couldn't be bothered to fight it, it would have been difficult…

– And very expensive emotionally…

– Oh, yes, and we 'd been getting very bored with each other for a long time; so I went to live with a friend of mine, she's got this eighteen-room country mansion, I stayed with her for five months, she did a lot of entertaining, and so I had a lovely life for a while…

– And your daughter?

– Oh, she's from my first marriage, a very good marriage, but my wife died…

– Oh, I'm sorry…you seem to get on well with women…

– Oh, yes, I like women – you know, Hélène, I am a good man, I am true, and I know what matters in life, and I don't pretend, what you see is what you get. I now live in a one-bedroom Housing Association flat and I think I'm lucky because I find life beautiful. I was driving back the other day, and there was the most amazing rainbow over the countryside, it's such a beautiful world, Hélène, and people are wonderful. You see, I am a graduate, I left LSE with a first. I have made money in the past, I used to work in advertising, but it's very soul-less, exhausting emotionally, and I couldn't do that any more...Now I do what matters to me. What do you want from life?

– I want to be happy with a man before I die...

– Don't be sad, sweetie...but it's true that I am probably useless to you, because you ask for a man who is solvent and I am not...

– So why did you reply to my ad?

– Because you ask for 'conversation'. And I thought: this is what she wants the most, the relationship, may be the rest isn't so vital, so I'll try...

– Let me tell you, Liam, I have earned money too, I've worked very hard and I've brought up my daughter on my own. But some years ago I lived with a man who very quickly fell terribly ill with heart disease and he was dying. To cut a very long story short, I found a healer who cured him, so he didn't need a transplant any longer, and as soon as he felt better he wanted to work again: so I financed him, and it cost me all my savings and some of my pension fund. I'm living on very little money. I would love to travel, have holidays, go to France which I miss a lot, and I can't, and I find it very frustrating.

– So I won't be able to live off you, will I? he quipped.

– No! So, you see, you are useless to me, I joked back, but I also see you are a good man and I would like us to meet...

– Maybe next week, Thursday possibly. What's your e-mail address?

*

– DINNER COMPANION WANTED, by Cambridge graduate, 50s, fit, active, enjoys human nature and wit. If you are attractive, intelligent and hungry, please reply. London.

Ross is back!! The doctor who lives on the river, who likes Anita Brookner's books, and whose voice seduced me early on in my quest; who suggested that we had dinner after a long and pleasant chat, but never rang me back. Obviously, he had met a woman he liked. I had mourned him somewhat: he had sounded so perfect – though a little young maybe? I now know, however, what 'perfect' on the telephone means: merely 'promising', until the promise is undone by unappealing looks, poor attitude, incompatible lifestyle, or lack of chemistry.

I noted he has altered his text slightly: he used to say: 'enjoys human nature, conversation and irony'. Why the change? 'Wit' is fine, but more general than 'irony', safer I feel. Did he get too many questions on the subject? Did anyone query whether 'irony' might have indicated a reticence on his part? Perhaps he got no questions at all...I know now that I may not like him when we meet, or he may not like me, of course; find me too old, apart from anything else. Still, his reappearance, probably indicating a short-lived romance, I find intriguing, and mustn't delay my call this time, I would enjoy meeting him at last.

When I left my message on his voice box, I couldn't resist telling him that we had spoken before – when was that? Six months ago at least... 'You suggested dinner, and then you disappeared, which was very bad of you!'

Of course I was one of the first to reply to his advert, and there would be many others. Still...our conversation was again lively, friendly, easy. His voice didn't strike me as so entrancing this time, which was just as well as I was also bracing myself for disappointment. After about forty minutes, he said: "You sound fun – would you like to come to see a play tomorrow night? I happen to have a spare ticket...the play starts at seven forty-five, we could meet at the entrance at seven and have a drink and a chat? Tell me again what you look like..."

I arrived first, enlivened at the prospect of an outing with an interesting man, but particularly as I would be making up for a past opportunity I had regretted missing. I decided to wear a black skirt and an open top which I had been told suited me, with a bright shawl over my coat. A good necklace.

A sporty-looking bald man came towards me holding out his hand:

– You look like Hélène! he exclaimed wittily.

– What a coincidence! I retorted, I happen to be Hélène!

We laughed and were friendly. He seemed to be happily surprised, and I was thrilled at his flattering glances. I was also disconcerted as I was finding myself immediately attracted to him, too rare an occurrence: Ross was a very male-looking male: five foot-ten, what was left of his remaining hair practically shaven, but the head was of good proportions, the square head of a warrior albeit with humorous eyes. He was slim and very fit-looking, which made me regret having deserted the gym and my recent indulgence with chocolate. He was wearing, under his dark blue Barbour coat, a simple and smart checked shirt.

He had parked his motorbike nearby – no congestion charge, no road tax, he commented – obviously a clever man about town. From our initial conversation I remembered that he played squash to keep fit, and it crossed my mind that he could be difficult to keep up with.

I was conscious of a semi-restrained smile on my face, in response to his examination of me, as well as an undisguised admission that I was stirred by it. I was suddenly feeling young and attractive, but more than that: I was a fully-fledged member – albeit for a short while probably – of the world I usually envied, the world of couples and of people who have the opportunity to go out and enjoy themselves in company.

I could still see us, standing at the bar: he was drinking a gin and tonic and I dared celebrate with a whisky (they are always small in this country), exchanging details about ourselves. This time, however, they seemed to be circumscribed by the present: typical of these meetings which have no past and usually no future. He asked about my book-writing, and had a lot to say about the book and publishing world: he had written a book a few years back, which he had published himself by starting a publishing company, and had been quite successful, appearing both on radio and television at the time. I was full of curiosity, also remembering that men like to shine. The conversation moved on to animals – yes, I liked them all, anything that moved. I also remembered that he had watched, from the window of his riverside flat, last February or March, the poor young whale that had lost its way in the Thames six months before, accompanied (and tortured by, I felt sure!) the constant roar of a television helicopter overhead and pitiless projector lights.

We eventually started to give each other a potted history of our lives and important relationships. It appeared he had never married – possibly shy of commitment, I pondered – but lived for many years with 'a partner' who had children; he still saw them occasionally.

– Oh, that's good, I commented, it's nice that you stayed close.

– Well, not that close, actually, we meet at funerals, that sort of thing…

– Oh…do you have any children of your own?

– No, he said with a dismissive pout, I've never really been interested…

I felt immediately convinced that there was a history

there, a sad childhood, a distant relationship with his parents, the lack of a vital bond...something that can make it difficult for two people to connect successfully, stopping them from being able "to deal with it".

The play was a comedy based on *The Thirty-Nine Steps* and such a masterpiece of comic genius that laughter made my cheeks ache. Glancing at him occasionally, I verified that he was equally amused. Keen to find out more about each other, we continued talking during the interval. It was only half past nine when the play finished. I felt happy and grateful for these moments and had a sensation of gliding, so elated was I. I wondered if we would go out to eat as for once I wasn't hungry, but he directed me towards Soho where he could use some vouchers he had been given. (I'd turned down his suggestion of the Marco Pierre White brasserie next to the theatre, finding it a little too pricey, since I insisted on paying for my share). We sat down, ordered fish, and pursued our conversation.

London had offered him a new life, it seemed, some years previously when his relationship failed, and a four-year affair with an attractive woman followed. She unfortunately "couldn't open up emotionally: I often tried to open this shell of hers, without success... . And if I did, there didn't seem to be anything there... . She was very much like my previous partner in this respect, actually."

– Ross, when you last advertised, about nine months ago, you and I spoke on the telephone, and you asked if I would have dinner with you but never rang again: did you meet someone then?

– Look, when people break up, sometimes they get back together...

– So that's what happened?

– Yes.

– And you are getting lots of replies this time?

– Yes… . He looked amused as he continued: there's a lot of sighing, they say: "Haah…what else can I tell you now, haah…?"

– And you meet many?

– A few…one of them was in her twenties, a charming girl, very bright. It's very interesting, you know…

Yes, I knew.

He could, of course, explore the whole of womankind. I wondered how academic his interest was:

– What do you want out of all this, Ross?

– A conversation.

– A conversation?

– A soul mate…

– Yes, for me too a relationship IS a conversation, in every sense of the word, heart, body and soul… . Tell me, how old was your previous lady?

– In her forties.

I don't stand a chance, I thought: he is fit and dynamic, curious about life, he can 'afford' a much younger woman than me…

– Tell me, now, Ross, I want to know more about your relationship…

Did he look anxious?

– …with Anita Brookner.

He seemed amused, almost relieved. I enjoyed teasing.

– Well, I like the way she writes, it is subtle, profound, and she gives you all the answers…

– After you mentioned her in our initial conversation, you know I have several books by her, I re-read some, and in one of them, I think it's *Undue Influence*, I'm not sure, she says, about the heroine: "…she had thought to do without love, only to be shown that love was on offer to those who knew how to deal with it."

He repeated the quote slowly, thoughtfully.

– I thought this was so profound, so true, don't you think, one has to be able to 'deal with it'…Ross, if you were to describe yourself…

I was going to add: what would you say? who are you? But the waitress was fussing over our table, taking away our plates, making idle chatter, and he asked for the bill. We were the last table on her patch, she obviously wanted us out. Ross put on his coat.

– Are you cold? I asked, surprised and somewhat annoyed, my fun was being curtailed.

– No, but I think we're being thrown out…

– I'd still like to be able to finish my sentence.

– I'm also working tomorrow…

– Oh, yes, you'll need your beauty sleep…I quipped, trying to keep my sudden bad humour light.

The night was still mild when we came out onto the street. I guessed it was quite late but didn't care. I felt part of the world. Ross, well-mannered, was walking me towards Leicester Square, where I'd mentioned I was taking the tube home.

– Ross, no, you don't have to, you know, I'm fine.

– Are you sure? Only my bike is in the other direction…

– I know, you said so; I'll be fine.

– All right, then, if you're sure.

– That was a good evening, Ross, thank you.

– Yes, I enjoyed it a lot, actually.

His face got closer and he kissed me on both cheeks. That's it, I thought, ships in the night again. He didn't say: I'll ring you, or: can I see you again? And I had so much more to say to him, so much to ask him about, the conversation wasn't finished, was it? I knew better than to protest. We were both aware he was merely at the beginning of his new quest, he was getting plenty of calls, and I had pathetically told him I was getting few:

– There's a lot of 'dead wood', so to speak, I don't meet many people…

However, walking through Leicester Square, I felt happy and invigorated. The area was still lively, mostly with young people, and there was much less of a crowd than I had anticipated, but it was late obviously. How late? Why, eleven-thirty! Time has passed so quickly.

*

Finding it hard to get to sleep, I picked up the book by Julian Barnes that 'my' millionaire had given me and attempted to plunge into yet another world. The cat, having had to wait longer than usual for his dinner, was all over me in excitement and gratitude and distracted me, pawing my stomach and my chest and purring down my face. In spite of my experience, it was still hard to believe that such a happy evening would very probably have no second chapter. I still had so many questions to ask him: who are you? tell me about your childhood, it must have been hard to have been sent away to boarding school (I know your type, you've learnt to repress your emotions the hard way, you are needy and can be difficult, you don't necessarily engage emotionally…you hurt others…) Tell me about your parents…

The role that Anita Brookner's books had played in his life was still a mystery to me: it couldn't be just a line that worked well with women? There is such desolation and loneliness there, does a part of you identify with that world? It must do. You had shown surprise when I had commented that many considered her 'a women's writer': are you one of the few men who don't make that distinction? And does it mean that you are prone to self-questioning and analysis yourself? Because it's so important to be able to examine oneself and others, I myself wouldn't be the person I am if I hadn't persisted in my natural bent for it. I had undergone therapy, of course, it's remarkable work, and I would've had to do it when I trained to become a counsellor anyway.

Barbara Pym was the other author he loved, I had heard of the name, what did she write? I would go to the nearby bookshop and order one of her books presently, I liked to know what I was talking about – which reminded me of Emmanuel, and more specifically of the healer who had saved his life: I had talked too much and too long about them both, this was premature, clumsy on my part: Ross was a doctor, a medical doctor, what did I think I was doing? It must have been like waving a red rag in front of a bull, and I had a small inkling of the effect my story was having when Ross had interrupted: 'And the healer did all that?' I had made a light-hearted gesture with my hand: 'I'm familiar with these things…' He might have been exasperated and dismissed me straight away. Did I unwittingly destroy my chances? On the other hand, this was a test to his openness of mind, albeit a premature one, but timing can be everything.

Recalling that first, and I am now convinced unique, meeting with Ross, I am struck again by his face and his assured manner: not for him the nervousness of the timorous, the panic of the shy. He had approached me with the cheerful assurance of a man who enjoyed the unpredictable and the adventurous:

– You look like Hélène!

There was a glint in his eyes, he enjoyed the game, the hunt ('I know it works,' he said later about the personal ads). His demeanour exuded youthful sexual energy; the way he looked at me, handing me my drink, was cheerfully forward, certainly confident of his manliness, and I was responding…

He had expressed surprise that I had seen his ad in the Saturday *Times*, since he had placed it in *Time Out*. I explained newspapers often seem to share these columns.

– Don't you buy *Time Out*? he was surprised.

– No, never…

– How do you know what's on, then? Still, I suppose you buy newspapers…

– Yes, I sometimes buy *The Times*, or the *Guardian*, at times the *Independent*…but I don't buy a paper every day.

– I find all you need to know about the world you learn from the morning news on the radio.

– Oh, no, you learn very little that way, you need all sorts of sources…I replied.

– Really? But if you read the papers you can't do anything else…

Yes, that was sometimes a problem, but it was a problem I enjoyed.

He knew I was probably older than him: he had asked what work I did and I mentioned interior design, I had taken a small job last year, which had been very frustrating, so I had decided to leave it and start to write…

– Did you find studying therapy helped you with interior design?

– Well, it was therapy for houses…

*

That night I had found it difficult to go to sleep, and got up early the next morning, full of vigour and desire to 'do'. I swept the patio of all its dead leaves; I then raked the lawn to make heaps of the gold and brassy litter that the trees had finally relinquished and disposed of them behind the curved bench that frames the garden at the back for future compost; the more I did, the more energy I seemed to accrue and I decided to sweep the front steps as well as clean the bedroom window sill. A visit to the garden centre suddenly appeared necessary: I needed a replacement for my agonising fatsia, as well as two small white cyclamens tinged with crimson for added flourish near the entrance door. Ignoring the washing up of the day before and a heap of ironing as not being worthy of my creative zest, I went for a long and glorious walk in Regent's Park, kicking the leaves as I went along and pretending to be a boy skipping class. I knew I wouldn't see Ross again and it didn't matter: I could now recognise where my feelings were best invested and it didn't seem to me there would be enough safety or nourishment in his hands. Today I could enjoy myself in my own company. Walking back home to do some work finally seemed both appealing and purposeful again.

*

I replied today to someone who was advertising himself as: USEFUL-LOOKING MAN…wondering what a useful man could look like – as opposed to a useless one! – was he wearing overalls and driving a white van? until I realised that the person taking down the message down misunderstood: 'YOUTHFUL-LOOKING MAN'…!

Chapter Twenty-three

Christmas is looming – we are going to drown again in tinsel, shiny baubles and for the most part false cheer, send dutiful cards, and the turkeys will come home to roast... I shall fill myself with patience and forbearance – I'm getting good at it – plan as many moments with friends as possible when they will be so busy themselves with their own families. Coming back from shopping this morning I noticed that my new neighbour next door has placed two entirely decorated small Christmas trees in her window box, a novel, childish and touchingly sweet idea which made me smile: she is a young woman and happy with her new home, bless her. I shall have no tree myself since my daughter no longer lives with me but will go and admire hers in her pretty flat. She doesn't miss an opportunity to celebrate her own happiness with Adam. I have made some rather attractive necklaces for my friends as well as Adam's mother and sister with whom we shall be spending Christmas day, and look forward to their surprise. I also have two parties lined up with my new Lib Dem friends and am learning to be more sociable. I shall join some classes at the City Lit in the New Year, I need to get out more. I shall go back to the gym.

There were no replies at all to my personal ads in the Saturday *Times* or the *Observer* last week, or the week before, and I need to reconsider my position: I might as well rewrite my own, emphasising my Frenchness this time. How about:

> FRANCOPHILE REQUIRED for spirited, warm, attractive, stylish Frenchwoman, young 60, into arts, ideas and good conversation, looking for caring, kind, educated fit man with French connections for LTR. London

I had been a little concerned of late as Liam, the sweet Irishman, hasn't rung or e.mailed me, and the more I thought about it, the more I was convinced that I had upset him and this was the cause of his silence. I thought I could trace it back to the part of our conversation where he said that he was probably useless to me because he wasn't solvent, and I told him about Emmanuel and how he siphoned off all my money, to end up agreeing that "yes, you are probably useless to me!" What a terrible thing to say to someone, just because he was broke. I felt quite ashamed.

Should I apologise? That meant ringing him, as I didn't have his address. Which meant talking to him directly since his mobile phone was always on, without the possible solution of leaving my apology in his absence, for him to ponder over and dispose of if he wished. He might think I was chasing him, although I doubted this as he had seemed so laid back, but being teased about it (a possibility) could be much worse. Nevertheless, the underlying idea was not to lose contact, how to achieve this with the minimum of embarrassment?

He might be quite simply angry with me, who had insulted him so casually. A man had his pride, particularly if he was a man of some worth and principles, and felt humiliated because he happened not to have sufficient financial means. He may have found me cold and arrogant, superficial even... . While he had shown himself to be a man of heart and warmth, in fact probably the nicest man I had spoken to on the telephone. And I rather liked being called 'sweetie'...

I couldn't decide how I would speak to him: what if he was busy and couldn't talk, or said, 'Can I ring you back in a minute, sweetie,' and never did?

– Hello, is that Liam?

– Yes.

– Hello, it's Hélène here...

– Oh, hello, sweetie. Look, can I ring you back in a minute or two, I'm in the middle of receiving an...

– No! I cried out in anguish. Listen, I have rung to apo...

– Oh, shit! I've lost it now, excuse my French, but – what is it?

– I think I have hurt your feelings...

– No, you haven't!

– Yes, I have...

– No, I assure you, you haven't, Hélène...

– But you said you'd ring back and you didn't, and you asked for my email address and I didn't hear from you...

– I have simply been very, very busy...

– Look, you answered my ad, and of course I talk to other people, and if I say I'll ring again, I do. Otherwise I don't, I have to mean what I'm saying and hope the other person does the same...

– I can only apologise, but you see, I work with a partner, and we work hard together, and when she's here we can't do anything else. Also, we're good friends, and she's been very dependent on me lately because she's been very badly messed around by a bloke and she needed support, you know what it's like…

– Yes, because that is friendship, and loyalty, that's good, but you and I had spoken and I have to be able to trust you…

– True, but I get totally engrossed in my work and can't think about anything else…

– And I feel now that you could've forgotten about me completely and never rung me again…

– Ah! That's quite possible…

– It's funny you saying that, because you were the one answering my ad, and you had sounded genuine when we first spoke, a man of heart…

– Well, I am…and I'm also sixty-two and three quarters, which is quite old…

– Well, you're also very unreliable!

– How are you getting on with your ad?

– Not terribly well…

– Why is that? What's wrong with 'them'?

– It's not that there is necessarily anything wrong with 'them', or 'me', it's that nothing happens BETWEEN us, no click…

– What are you doing tomorrow?

– Tomorrow? Well, I'm going to a friend's exhibition…why?

– I may be coming to London for the day, there's a show at Olympia I need to see, maybe we could meet for a couple of hours and have lunch…

– Well, I could see my friend's exhibition the following day I suppose…

– I'll tell you what, I'll ring you tomorrow morning at half past nine to confirm if I'm coming to London or not.

– All right, if you say so…

– I promise I will.

My conversation with Liam had left me disheartened: I was, in the first instance and contrary to my normal feelings, somewhat disappointed that he hadn't felt upset as this would had confirmed to me that he was a man of honour and pride. Instead he had shown himself to be possibly superficial – charmingly but irrevocably – and capable of the erratic behaviour usually more attributable to an adolescent: I had been warned. Nothing very serious could be expected from a relationship with Liam but I would see whether he rang me the following day.

When the telephone rang the next morning, a dank dark day of early December, I looked at the clock which indicated very precisely half past nine.

– Hélène?

– Yes, good morning Liam.

– And good morning to you, Hélène! I'm afraid I won't be coming today but very likely Thursday or Friday: can we meet then? Are you free during the day?

– I can be...

– Right, I'll ring you on Thursday morning to let you know.

– Okay, but I won't ring you again, it's up to you now.

– Okay. Bye...

*

Liam never called back, and neither did I.

Chapter Twenty-four

Something strange happened one day this summer. Although it would be closer to the truth to say that very little really happened, I am still pinching myself, as I try to come to terms with he fact that I actually met a man on a date, who had just left prison for, I am now convinced, the murder of his wife…

In the message he left in my voice box, John had sounded interesting if a little dry, matter-of-fact. Unpretentious at least. He'd had a career as a professional man, indicating some knowledge and an understanding of the world. Not a bourgeois, his position was quite left-wing and his manner down-to-earth: he simply declared that he was looking for a life partner, having been divorced of a first wife and widowed of a second. A few children, all grown up. He was retired, had money, a house in a very nice part of London and a cottage in the country where he thought he might live, and he wanted to meet me.

My imagination is always quick to run away with me for a short while, as the mention of the country cottage made me wonder if I could then keep some chickens, which would be just lovely…

*

Very tall, slim, with a craggy face and a thick mop of white hair, dressed simply in a pair of jeans and a blue shirt, John looked quite reasonable for his age (very close to mine) despite the lack of effort. Since he'd come by bicycle, the casual attire was appropriate and besides, it was nearly midsummer, hot, and he didn't stand out from the crowd assembled outside that lovely pub near Regent's Park.

– Are you Hélène? He looked serious.

– Yes, hello John.

I smiled as we shook hands. The crowd of drinkers around us was so cheerfully noisy that we decided to step along the road, and stopped when we saw a single table and two chairs outside a delicatessen. We sat down. We could've done better I felt, but got a sense that he was possibly in a hurry, although it could have been his brusque manner. He came back with two cups of tea and we chatted, but there was still no sign of a smile, even as we talked about this lovely area he knew well as a student, and the happy crowds of summer.

– You said you go to classes?

– Oh yes, I replied, and started describing the wonderful two-year playwriting course I had just finished, we were a dedicated bunch and our tutor was outstanding.

– And what's your play about?

Glad that he'd asked, I explained: Well, a man in his mid-fifties comes back from Australia where he was a farmer, after a painful divorce and leaving his children behind. A difficult man, resentful of his sister and traumatised in his past by a violent father, he loses the childhood friend he falls in love with because of his own violence… . There you are.

He was shaking his head in appreciation and understanding, and I was gratified: I'd always wanted to meet someone who was interested in what I do. There were already, however, two big hurdles: he never smiled or laughed, and talking had revealed a dreadful set of teeth, crooked and yellowy-grey, which I found horribly off-putting; how could anyone ever kiss someone with such bad teeth?

Perhaps I should try not to look at them when he spoke, just concentrate on the words. Still, that was easier said than done, but his eyes, blue and wide-open, gave him an innocent look and spoke of childhood unfinished. He too attended classes, the concurrence of globalisation and warfare fascinated him, and I appreciated his intelligence, his curiosity, his desire to share. He also spoke about his country cottage where he planned to live, but it needed work...

– Maybe you can help me?

I was startled: how could he presume? Surely he was joking? I hadn't shown any sign of liking him as a man, I had merely been friendly, but was this confusing for him? And he wasn't the joking type, so what was this about? It got drowned in questions about the dating 'game': had I had many replies? He himself had an ad appearing the following week: Oh, you'll be busy, then! I joked. When I asked if he had children, he replied:

– Hum, yes...in layers.

I laughed. Nice way of putting it, and I knew what he meant. I told him of my long-ago marriage and divorce, and my one and lovely daughter.

– Would you like to tell me more about your life, John?

– Hum...I'll tell you on our third meeting, if you still wish to see me again...it's...complicated...

Fair enough, I thought, if he wants to wait before talking of difficult things. Many of us have complicated lives but I was curious, and I like a story. He looked at me boldly:

– How do you know when you like a man, Hélène?

I felt rushed, withdrew.

– Oh, I said sternly, there needs to be real chemistry, a true connection...

– And, do you...? he moved his hand between us a few times, reluctant or unable to use words.

– Good God! I exclaimed primly. It's far too early!

I walked him back to his bicycle. A very fit man, obviously, not intimidated by the London traffic. We said goodbye without making plans, and I made my way back home. That man seemed to like me, yet I hadn't *felt* it; there had been nothing of the glances, smiles, gestures, to indicate that this was the case, and so his words had seemed incongruous. John was intelligent but obviously didn't do charm. And those terrible teeth...

A few days later, my telephone rang: John wanted to meet me. It was a beautiful evening and his offer much better than staying in, I thought. I suggested a small Greek restaurant I knew. Maybe he would tell me more about his life? I had been conscious of not really wishing to confide in him very much myself, maybe it was his coldness, somehow the 'terrain' wasn't right. And he'd asked very little about me, only about my play, in fact.

Shared food and a glass of wine helped, and as we were sitting at a right angle to each other, he was expanding on his new political interests, until I diverted him towards his childhood: it had meant boarding school of course, as befitted a child of wealthy but cold and conventional parents, and he'd retained terrible memories of it, never felt accepted, was badly bullied too.

That's right, I thought, that fits, he's like a dog that never wags its tail...

Our main dish, a moussaka, was disappointing.

– I can do much better myself, he commented.

– You cook?

– Yes, I enjoy it.

That's more than I can say, as I haven't got much inclination to cook if there's no one to share the meal with. In my books, the man who cooks is a gem. Except that usually the person who enjoys food will be animated while talking about it, reminisce, anticipate…

When we came out, the evening glowed with the softness and warmth of midsummer; families, friends and couples were scattered all over the park, many with picnics and blankets, little children laughing and running about.

– You want to walk a bit?

– That'd be nice.

And we merged with the happy crowds. I learned a few more details about him that evening: his father, an army officer, educated at Sandhurst, had been strict and distant, showing little interest in his son, and left the family when John was four years old to marry someone else. I could tell by the tone of his voice that John had been in awe of him. His mother he remembered as kind, but he was sent to boarding school anyway.

We sat on the grass. It was easy to feel happy for the air was mild and the scenery beautiful. Although I couldn't say John didn't enjoy it, he seemed the only person there who didn't seem happy. It wasn't the first time, far from it, that I'd met such a man, so obviously hurt by his past that he didn't know how to express feelings or show any warmth. I seemed to 'collect' such men, or at least attract them. They often were very frustrating if not destructive.

When he seemed to go silent, I butted in:

– Shall I make you laugh? Shall I tell you who I *won't* be meeting this week?

– If you like…

– Well, I got this call, a researcher, ex-teacher and

occasional writer, who lives not very far away from here... . He noticed my accent, so I admitted to being French, and he went delirious: Ahh!...I would *worship* you!! And while feeling that a little worship wouldn't go amiss, you know, I thought it was a bit over the top, don't you think? For an Englishman?

I was all the more cheerful that I felt completely detached. I knew John was completely wrong for me and didn't experience the slightest attraction. Yes he was clever, quite interesting and had beautiful, thick, white hair (badly cut). But the teeth...and the coldness! I could hardly take his jerking of the head and strangled Ha! for a burst of laughter.

– And do you know, I went on, what he asked me at the end of our chat?

He said: And do you own many pairs of shoes?

I replied: Probably, but not the kind you mean, I think....A shoe fetishist!

John seemed aghast:

– But what do they **do**?

I had to confess my ignorance. The evening was coming to a close.

– You'll walk me back to my car? I suggested.

– You came by car? he said severely. But you live so close! You should've walked! You should walk everywhere! You're very lazy!

– I was afraid of being late, I lied.

I didn't like being ticked off like a little girl. Not at my age. Not at any age. Even if he was right. And when he bent down to give me a goodbye kiss, I turned my head away and he only got my cheek. What a nerve.

*

That was that, I concluded. No big deal...except that the summer was in a good mood that week. Except that day by day, life was passing me by. Shouldn't I try harder? Even with my writing seemingly progressing well, even sitting in my beautiful garden, I was lonely.

It was a Friday, early afternoon: what if I rang John? He might tell me the rest of his story?

– Would you like to come for a drink in my garden?

– Oh yes, yes...certainly. I have a class at six, but I could come for two or three hours...

Good, I thought, he'll come, and then he'll go.

He'd come by public transport (no kiss hello, no greetings) and, being hot, asked straightaway if he could use the bathroom to freshen up. He went there directly. Not the type to tiptoe, John on the contrary walked as if he owned the place. You could read his will in the certainty of his movements, the strength of his steps. Used to the outdoors? Or used to owning the place? The power of money taking away all doubt? When he came out, I was ready with a tray, glasses, and fruit juice for myself since he'd brought some beer, and we stepped into the garden.

I sat in my deckchair, and watched with surprise as he removed his shirt, revealing his very fit, naked torso. Looking sternly at him, I raised an eyebrow. I just knew he wanted to show me how good he still looked and inspire desire.

– Is that all right?

– Well...as long as you don't take off anything else!

– Isn't it what soulmates are supposed to do?

He was looking at me fixedly. Silenced by his boldness, I merely raised my eyes to the sky and filled my glass. The man didn't do subtlety, but although I could be quite direct myself, I was stunned. He sat down and opened a can of beer. I wanted to change the subject:

– Don't you think I have a beautiful garden?

– It's a Very Beautiful Garden! he exclaimed with great emphasis. I didn't care that he didn't pay me any compliments, but anyone who doesn't admire my garden is beyond the pale. Deciding to remain in neutral, I mentioned his London house, how long had he had it? Oh, ages, but it was on the market, and he was staying with his ex-wife when he was in London, she was his best friend. At least that spoke well for him. He spent his weekends at his cottage, clearing the grounds, cutting the brambles, there was a lot to do.

– Are you sure you won't need a pad in London, now you'll be meeting all these ladies? I asked mischievously.

– Ah, but it's different now, because I've met you…

I was speechless, not one of my usual characteristics. He was staring at me provocatively.

– What does that feel like?

– Like pressure, I replied, irritated.

Yes, pressure. It certainly wasn't a declaration of love, and it was more than mere provocation, it seemed to be a declaration of intent that hadn't even taken my views into account! How could he possibly assume that I was attracted to him?

Extraordinary, I thought. The man is a bully. Arrogant, selfish, and possibly very needy as well. Maybe women found him attractive: he was tall and fit after all, with a strong presence and overtly sexual, he must have been lucky with them. Perhaps it was having money that gave him that insolence – and many men are afflicted with bad teeth after all…I was aware of feeling irritated now. I looked at him:

– Do you cut your own hair, John?

– Why? Does it show?

– Oh! Of course.

– Really?

– Why don't you go to a hairdresser? Are you stingy?
It doesn't need to cost very much, you know…

– Oh…

– I have my hair trimmed every three weeks. I feel it's
important to look as neat as possible…

– Did you notice my teeth were all crooked?

I shrugged and opened my hands in a gesture of the
utmost tolerance: it takes restraint for me not to dissolve
into giggles.

– It's very common…many people have quite bad
teeth…I myself had a few irregular teeth fixed a few years
ago. You know, we don't exactly get any prettier as we
age, so it matters even more to look decent …

– And how much did it cost?

I told him, and he shook his head slowly. I added:

– Many dentists do cosmetic work nowadays, you know,
it's very common… . You have money, it won't be a
problem.

He nodded. I looked at him. I sensed he'd temporarily
lost his brashness.

– Would you like to tell me your story now, John?

A frown appeared on his forehead.

– As I said before, it's complicated…

– Yes?

– I…I've not been back in London very long…

– Yes…where were you before?

– In jail…

– Really? I felt quite steady, waited. These things can
happen.

– As I've said to you before, I am divorced from my
first wife. We had two children…

– Yes?

– Some years later, I married again…a much younger
woman…we'd been together for some years already…we

were very much in love, very happy…we had a child, four at the time, a gorgeous boy. We practically spent our life on holiday. I didn't need to work, you see, I have plenty of money. …And then one day, completely out of the blue – we were happy, and I adored her… – out of the blue, one morning, she says to me: I'm not going to live with you any more. Just like that! I was horrified: WHY? I could see no reason…I asked her not to leave me, promised her I'd do anything to keep her, I wanted nothing but her, she couldn't do that to me…but she was adamant…and I felt completely lost, crying, promising her anything…I just couldn't bear the thought…I tried to kill myself, in the car, with the exhaust fumes, but it didn't work. For some reason it didn't work… . She insisted she wanted a divorce, and eventually she left, moved into a flat…I was beside myself…not knowing what to do. We shared the child, you see, I looked after him half the time, but it was so hard…and my wife wanted our son in private school, and I hated that, I can't stand the system, I'd gone to private school myself, I knew what it was like…we had lots of arguments about it.

One morning, after taking the child to school, she dropped by… . She wanted to discuss things about the divorce, she was very greedy, you know, wanted a lot of money, a share of my properties…I felt she was greedy…lots of people said she'd married me for the money, maybe it's true, but we were happy, we did things together, our sex life was very good… . God, we had sex all the time! I just couldn't understand… . Anyway, we talked for a while, and as she left, she said could I keep an eye on her car for a minute? I didn't understand why, but anyway… . And it was the last time I saw her! She never came back! She disappeared! Of course the police thought I'd done it…killed her I mean. They searched the house everywhere, and the cottage, and the grounds, even my ex-wife's house and garden...never found her. I knew she was dead, I just knew it, you see, she would never have left our child...the police asked me how I knew, but she just adored the boy, she would never have gone anywhere without him... . That's why I knew she must be dead...

I had become concerned that his voice was carrying much further than my garden walls.

– John, excuse me, but could you keep your voice down, I'm sure all the neighbours must hear you...

– I don't care! I've been through all this and I don't care any more...

– John, **I** live here, and **I** care, don't just think of yourself, keep your voice down, please...

His eyes were full of tears, and he wiped his cheeks.

– If you want me to go, just say so...

– No, no, you don't have to go, just keep your voice down, please...so what happened?

– The police never found her body, and the jury couldn't agree on a verdict. They had to drop the case. That was about ten years ago now...

– But you went to jail, you said?

– You see, sometimes, after a few years, there's a judicial review, so they took up the case again, and it went to court, and the police were still convinced I'd done it... He opened his hands in a gesture of surrender to fate. My lawyer said it: it's simple abuse of process... . They had no proof, they'd never found her body... . They said all kinds of things, that I was dominating, or domineering... . Anyway, they sent me down for manslaughter. Seven years. So I was away for three and a half.

Right, I thought, if it went to court, it should be on the internet, I'll look it up.

– Where did you go?

– Belmarsh, to start with... He opened another can of beer.

– How was it?

– Not so bad, actually... He turned to me. I remembered this was the boy who'd been sent to boarding school. It's not as bad as they say, you know, the other inmates were very kind... . After a couple of years, I was sent to an open prison.

– So when did you come out, then?

– Last April.

I was very conscious that John had been telling me only a small part of his story, the part that suited the moment. Maybe the part he wanted to believe, for he needed to survive on his own terms. Whichever it was, whatever the fate of his young wife – and if she was never found, after all this time, it was a very near certainty that she was dead, I surmised – he himself had a terrible time: her loss, even at his own hands, would have been devastating. Only some of his pride could have been salvaged, but there would have been no peace for him in all these years.

– You know, John, what I'm thinking...I'm aware that you haven't been back long... .You've been through a dreadful time, a lot of trauma, and it must be very difficult for you, for anyone, to readjust to real life after all that... . What I'm thinking would be useful, is for you to see a psychotherapist...someone to talk to, feel supported, who could help you find your feet again...

– You think so, do you?

– Yes, I do. Seriously. I had therapy myself in the past and it helped me enormously. You're entering a new life, you know, you'll need to be equipped properly, find meaning and purpose...

We were in June. Midsummer in all its glory, at least for a few days...and John had a practical, well-organised mind. He knew his needs and had set about trying to fulfil them by finding himself a woman, quickly: sex, maybe love, was his prime need, but he needed help, and to look at himself in depth maybe, too. He looked at his watch:

– I must be on my way. My class. Don't like to be late.

I got up as well. I was suddenly feeling very tired. We walked back to the flat and he put his shirt back on. Before buttoning it up, he put his arms around me. I stiffened.

– I think it's about time you and I started touching each other.

– I don't think so, John…what do you want anyway?

– I want a physical relationship. He was holding me tight.

– I know that! But I want far more than that, I want the whole thing and I don't think…

– You make a difference?

– I certainly do!

– I'm loving you now… he insisted. Because he was bending his head to kiss me, I was keeping my head down, and felt a series of small kisses on my forehead. I pushed him away gently, saying:

– Don't be late now. How're you getting there?

– Oh, on the tube, it's easy enough…doesn't take very long.

– Bye now.

– Bye.

I closed the door, went to the sink and poured myself a large glass of water. What an afternoon. And I went and sat at my computer, turning the internet on.

*

I cannot say any of it was too much of a surprise, in fact it all made sad sense, but the tragedy the articles were recounting was overwhelming in its horror and apparent inevitability. The facts, as they appeared to the prosecution, the police, and the press in general, didn't jar with what John had told me, so in a way he could claim to have told me the truth. He had merely been very economical with it. He had always denied killing his wife, and it was never proven that he did, since repeated searches failed to find her body, and there is such a thing as denial... . However, the presumption that she was dead was reinforced by several other factors: her bank accounts remained untouched, and in all the years that passed, she never once made contact with her close family or her young son, attempted to visit her home or retrieve her car which was left outside John's house that fateful morning.

After she left, he faxed her a message at her sister's, reiterating that he would do anything to win her back, and ended "somewhat ominously", said the prosecution, writing that: "I can foresee no prospect of happiness remotely equivalent of the distress I would suffer in the loss of my wife and child, and my future actions will be directed to minimizing distress. This isn't a threat, it's common sense."

Their young boy's education had been a source of extreme conflict, as John had an intense dislike of private education – he himself was sent as a child to the same boarding school as his father's, where he was extremely unhappy, and now his wife had enrolled the boy at a private school. Together with their disputes over money, the tensions between them, through their respective lawyers and also face to face, were very high, but I felt it was despair that filled him and his inability to overcome the childhood terror of being abandoned. He set up a shrine on a landing table where he surrounded a photograph of her with an arrangement of flowers. He later sobbed in front of her sister, saying: "She's dead, she's dead, what am I going to do now? I loved her so much." Asked how he knew she was dead, he replied: "I just know it. She would never have left our child."

While the court heard of John's insistence that: "women must never leave me", it was later revealed that he also had a history of violence, and this the jury was never allowed to hear about. A wealthy man, tall, slim and forward in his manner, considered by some to be eccentric, by others "arrogant and supercilious", he often met women in bars, or through an ad he placed in a Sunday newspaper where he advertised himself as looking for love. John had two other children through some of these relationships, but a previous girlfriend had accused him of beating her up and attempted rape and sought a court injunction to keep him away from her. On another occasion, which the jury was told about, John had laughed as he told his sister-in-law that his wife had been forced to buy sunglasses to hide her black eyes after one attack on holiday. Several women who had relationships with him described him as verbally and physically violent, and he declared to one of them: "Women must never leave me…that's when the trouble starts."

*

Trouble indeed. I felt I understood. After his cold and dominant father left the family home one Christmas day, never to return, the four-year old he was then must have lived in a panic that his mother could leave him as well, and clung to her for dear life. A terrible insecurity inhabited him, never to relent. He later had to prove to himself that he could attract and seduce women, and they must never leave him. He was no stranger to violence, as I would think he must have been hit by his father as a child, in this he was no rare exception at the time. His mother also betrayed him by sending him away, and the separation from her must have been near unbearable, particularly as his father never visited. Experiencing loneliness as well as bullying at boarding school would have confirmed him in his view of the world, and violence and pain were a necessary part of it.

I understood. And I could easily believe what the police believed, that somewhere not too far from his house, the body of a woman lay undiscovered, maybe for ever, because she refused to be dominated, bullied, beaten, and wanted to build a sane life away from him. And that because of what he did to her, their small child would forever be without his mother.

You cannot call just anything love. Indeed need can seem a close substitute, the compulsion to possess, and this is where I seemed to fit, not so incongruously, in the story: the man was intelligent, knowledgeable, practical and rational as well. He knew he couldn't properly function without a woman, therefore he must find himself one and get organised. It never seemed to matter very much to John who I was: he wanted a physical relationship, a way of merging with another, who must never leave him. Whatever my feelings, thoughts and tastes were, they appeared irrelevant to him, as he never consulted me, which I found astonishing. I was an object. In his mind, I must have fitted a broad template of his kind of woman: warm, with the right sort of background, reasonably attractive and intelligent: I would do. He was prepared to be 'in love'.

A couple of weeks later, John rang. He sounded frantic:

– Hélène! I'd lost your phone number! I've only just found it!"

– John, listen…I don't think it's a good idea for us to meet again…"

– Ah! …Oh…all right, I see…"

– Bye John." And I put the telephone down.

Was it the end, then? I felt a slight tremor. Not that I'd ever really felt threatened, but I'd been a little shaken, yes. After all, it could have turned out much worse. However, in as much as logic necessarily plays the dominant part in these stories, I think I was safe because he hadn't possessed me: he didn't lose much, there were other women out there. One of them would eventually fall for whatever he had to offer, alas, and I wish I could send her a message: "Don't! Don't go near him! Don't let him dominate you! I have a story to tell you!" And I would tell her what I've written here, so maybe she'll hear…

Looking back, it strikes me as ironic – and if he'd known how to 'read' others, he could have taken it on board – that the first intimate thing I told him about me, through the theme of a play I had only recently written, was that the protagonist, who had left his family to get away from a violent father, loses the woman he falls in love with on his return because of his own violence. There was a lesson the protagonist hadn't learnt, but which I had: that no one, no man in particular, would take advantage of me, use me, ignore me, as had often happened in the past. And about time, too, at my age.

Chapter Twenty-Five

I am getting old.

No, it is more subtle and insidious than that: I am wilting. Slowly, you might say gently on a good day. But irretrievably, which will touch and sadden those I know who are truly fond of me, like my daughter, and somewhere appeal to their sense of the fragility of life and make them feel a little protective, a little indulgent of my occasional feistiness and bluster. I value them all the more since that calamitous French 'holiday' early last summer with Eliane whom I had always considered my closest friend,

*

It took me two weeks after I got back home, so choked was I with hurt and disbelief, before I could put the whole picture together in words that made sense and talk about it to anyone. I felt terribly wounded at Eliane's repeated attempts to demean me. I made a list of all the incidents, all her remarks: how could a woman who behaved this way possibly love me as a friend? What was the matter with her? And how could I be so betrayed again? It all reminded me so much of my old relationship with my mother, in whose declared love I had so often sought childlike refuge, only to be systematically condemned and rejected by her. Whenever she initiated confidences, I always believed I would be understood, but it only ever proved to be a trap...I was stunned, and too hurt to cry.

Yet Eliane was a usually perceptive woman, who would have acquired self-knowledge during six years of analysis when she was young, or so I had thought. Maybe she had stopped examining herself, and some things in me had triggered this avalanche of criticism and rejection: apart from my appearance which seemed to be of more concern to her than it was to me, maybe she felt I had a future – a tentative future at that stage – while her own life was now predictable with her boring husband. I might meet someone new, love again, make a new life, possibly be happy: did she resent that already? I had also finally started writing seriously at last, and felt hopeful in a way I had never done before as I had been getting good feedback on my work: was this not acceptable?

So, I am getting old, who is being spared? A sly and insidious new map is very subtly carving itself on my face and body, and it isn't so much the creases I deplore as the landslides.... .There are the battle scars too: a persistent mark from a burn on my hand (ironing), the hollows around the eyes left by a bad bronchitis some years ago; the overall roundness of my body caused by my fondness of chocolate. My chin is showing bad intentions and the frown that has lived for years between my eyes is getting deeper; my cheeks are sliding down and I will also probably develop varicose veins.... . Do I have to let it all haunt me? I will just take care of myself and pursue my goals, since it seems I have acquired some in recent years, and I will continue to fight my battles.

I cannot hate Eliane, but I am hurt. I love what we were but the friendship met its end in that brutal attack.

I feel at once bereaved and unexpectedly strong for I am no longer frightened to love a man who would be unkind or harmful to me, I know I just wouldn't stand for it. Indeed my new ad, now requesting 'a Francophile', is bringing me a small number of extremely interesting and pleasant men (a senior university lecturer, a psychotherapist, a musician and writer...) I am due to meet the first two next week, the third one next month as he lives in France.

All this leaves me pensive, expectant: if I should, by chance – and effort – be lucky enough to meet a good man who could be my dearest friend and lover, I would recognise it this time, and seize the opportunity with both hands. I have changed.

I look back decades ago to an old image of me, a very lonely student in my twenties, sitting at a pavement café in Bordeaux, waiting for nothing; a summer's afternoon, with an implacable sun, in crude contrast with my almost permanent sense of drowning in solitude. I recall feeling like a thing, an object, among the marble-topped tables and the cane chairs, a nearby flower-stall providing the scents. The waiters danced among the tables, bringing ice-cream and pastel drinks; heavy buses and shiny cars, full of purpose, hurried past. Then I caught sight of a young man, not much older than me, sitting alone quite close by; his stillness, like solid silence, seemed to shroud him from the world, as if his presence was absence.

He started writing – on grey paper, in large letters – his pain, his plight and need: "The days are becoming impossible, and the nights more difficult still, this loneliness is an absurd misunderstanding."

He was a prisoner of it, I feel, as I was of my own solitude: a slow building of silent walls had erected another prison inside ourselves, as outside. I didn't even contemplate that his message could be for me: the prospect of a miracle was too remote a hope and too hurtful an admission for me to consider a reason to live otherwise. And so I went, leaving him there with his lonely vision, and taking mine nowhere.

But that was then. I am by now well used to losses and more willingly accept the renewal that still loving people brings with it: we are seasonal beings, and the new season is bringing other friends and a little hope. I think I have learnt, and would now be able to 'deal with it': I am living my life, and it is not over.

THE END